W9-AFC-034

DISCARDED

THE WORLD OF REPTILES

By Richard Carrington

A GUIDE TO EARTH HISTORY

MERMAIDS AND MASTODONS

THE TEARS OF ISIS

EAST FROM TUNIS

ELEPHANTS

A BIOGRAPHY OF THE SEA

A MILLION YEARS OF MAN
(Weidenfeld & Nicolson)

THE MAMMALS
(Time Inc. Book Division)

By Angus Bellairs

REPTILES (Hutchinson)

Emerald tree-boa (*Boa canina*)

THE WORLD OF REPTILES

ANGUS BELLAIRS

AND

RICHARD CARRINGTON

NEW YORK

AMERICAN ELSEVIER PUBLISHING COMPANY, INC.

CARL A. RUDISILL LIBRARY
LENOIR RHYNE COLLEGE

© ANGUS BELLAIRS AND
RICHARD CARRINGTON 1966

FIRST PUBLISHED 1966
AMERICAN ELSEVIER PUBLISHING COMPANY, INC.
52 VANDERBILT AVENUE
NEW YORK 17, NEW YORK

598.1
B 41 w
61386
April 1968

LIBRARY OF CONGRESS CATALOG CARD NUMBER 66-17674

PRINTED IN GREAT BRITAIN BY
MORRISON AND GIBB LTD
LONDON AND EDINBURGH

CONTENTS

ACKNOWLEDGEMENTS

We are indebted to the many people who have helped us over the preparation of this book. Miss S. V. Poyntz, Mr R. Bustard and Mr P. Pritchard have given us valuable advice on certain topics. Figures 1, 5, 7, 10 and 25 were drawn, or adapted from other authors, by Miss L. A. Holder, figures 18 and 19 by Mr W. Graham, and figure 15 by Mr John Norris Wood. Acknowledgements for photographs are made to the following individuals, institutions, and agencies: New York Zoological Society for Plates 1a, 2a, 3b, 4a and 5a; Frederic Lewis Inc. for Plates 1b, 4b and 15b; Mr Frank Lane's agency for Plates 2b, 7b, 8a, 9b, 10a, 11b, 12a and 13a; Mr William Hosmer and the American Museum of Natural History for Plates 3a, 10b and 11a; Zoological Society of London for Plates 5b, 6b, 8b and 9a; Mr Charles M. Bogert for Plate 6a; and Paul Popper Ltd. for Plates 7a, 12b, 13b, 14, 15a, 16a and 16b.

PLATES

7

PLATES

13 a. Male combat dance of red diamond rattlesnakes (*Crotalus ruber ruber*).
  b. Puff adder (*Bitis arietans*) showing its fangs.
14. African cobra (*Naja melanoleuca*). The glottis can be seen in the mouth.
15 a. Nile crocodile (*Crocodylus niloticus*).
  b. American crocodile (*Crocodylus acutus*) on left, and alligator (*Alligator mississippiensis*).
16 a. False or Schlegel's gharial (*Tomistoma schlegeli*) of Borneo and Malaya.
  b. Marsh crocodile or mugger (*Crocodylus palustris*) of India.

FIGURES IN THE TEXT

9

THE WORLD OF REPTILES

INTRODUCTION

WE have tried in this book to give a general introduction to what is known about the living reptiles of the world—how they are classified, how their bodies work, and what kind of lives they lead. These scaly, creeping or swimming creatures form one of the great divisions, or classes, of vertebrates, the 'animals with backbones'; the others are the various classes of fishes, the amphibians, the birds and the mammals. Approximately six thousand species of reptiles exist today, distributed among four main groups or orders: the tortoises and turtles (with about 250 species), the crocodilians (25 species), the lizards and snakes (with 5,700 species divided almost equally between them), and an order which contains only a single species, the tuatara of New Zealand.

These animals are the survivors of a much wider range of reptiles which lived in ancient times. The reptiles first evolved from amphibian ancestors about 280 million years ago, and became in quite a short period of geological time the predominant form of vertebrate life. During the era of the earth's history known as the Mesozoic, which lasted from about 225 million to 70 million years ago, they flourished in immense variety and abundance over the greater part of the earth's surface. The fossil record of those times shows that many early reptiles were as small as present-day lizards; but others, such as the famous dinosaurs, the ichthyosaurs and plesiosaurs of the oceans, and the flying pterosaurs, were bizarre, highly specialised creatures, often of enormous size. Towards the end of the Mesozoic era these animals died out, and their place was taken by the birds and mammals, which themselves had evolved from two separate branches of the reptile stock.

Some of these remarkable extinct reptiles are shown in Fig. 1 on the opposite page, which explains how the various groups of reptiles are related to each other and to the other classes of vertebrates. It will certainly add to our interest in the living types of reptiles if we remember that they are survivors of a great dynasty which flourished for millions of years, and which has lasted for a period vastly longer than our own human species.

Compared with the gay and active birds and the mammals with their greater human appeal, the living reptiles have been somewhat neglected by naturalists. An emotional dislike of reptiles may well be partly responsible for this, and even the great eighteenth-century naturalist Linnaeus described them as 'foul and loathsome' creatures. "They are abhorrent," he says, "because of their cold body, pale colour, cartilaginous skeleton, filthy skin, fierce aspect, calculating eye, offensive smell, harsh voice, squalid habitation, and terrible venom; wherefore their Creator has not exerted his powers to make many of them."

Although this verdict of Linnaeus is now generally recognised as being exaggerated and in many respects untrue, it is well known that reptiles still arouse deep and complicated feelings in many people. They are feared with some justification, for many of them are dangerous, and can kill swiftly by the apparently mysterious means of injecting venom. Their movements are also strange and somehow rather frightening. Their very name comes from the Latin *repere*, to creep, and the slow creeping movements of some reptiles have certainly helped to inspire fear. They have also been associated since prehistoric times with many supernatural beliefs. Some of these have been quite sympathetic or even encouraging, such as the idea that a snake may be a symbol of healing or contain the spirit of an ancestor; but some, it must be admitted, have shown the reptile in an evil or sinister role. To take only one instance

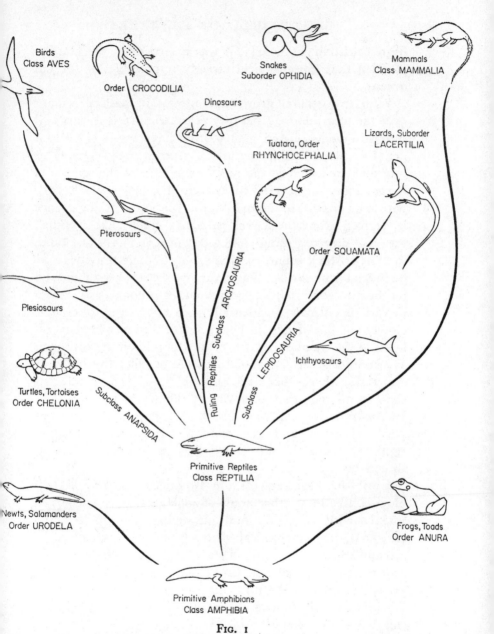

Birds
Class AVES

Order CROCODILIA

Dinosaurs

Snakes
Suborder OPHIDIA

Mammals
Class MAMMALIA

Tuatara, Order
RHYNCHOCEPHALIA

Lizards, Suborder
LACERTILIA

Pterosaurs

Plesiosaurs

Order SQUAMATA

Ruling Reptiles Subclass ARCHOSAURIA

Subclass LEPIDOSAURIA

Ichthyosaurs

Turtles, Tortoises
Order CHELONIA

Subclass ANAPSIDA

Primitive Reptiles
Class REPTILIA

Newts, Salamanders
Order URODELA

Frogs, Toads
Order ANURA

Primitive Amphibians
Class AMPHIBIA

FIG. 1

Diagram showing the relationships of the main groups of reptiles.

from Christian mythology, it was a serpent in the Garden of Eden that must be held directly responsible for the fall of man.

With the general growth of interest in natural science over the past hundred and fifty years, the magical fears and superstitions associated with reptiles have given place to a genuine interest in the nature of reptiles themselves. This interest is reflected in the rapid expansion of the science of herpetology, the specialised branch of zoology which deals with both reptiles and amphibians. The name of this science is derived from the Greek *herpeton*, which, like 'reptile', means 'a creeping thing', and today herpetologists are found in most civilised countries. The extent of their activities may be judged from the fact that in the year 1961, over a thousand publications on reptiles appeared either as books or as articles in various journals. Incidentally, it is interesting to see how closely our knowledge of the reptiles of different lands is related to the number of naturalists who inhabit or visit them. We know a great deal about the reptiles which live in North America, where there are probably more herpetologists than in all the other countries of the world put together. In Australia, on the other hand, such naturalists are comparatively rare, and that country's rich and fascinating reptilian fauna is still much less well known than it should be.

Until the beginning of the twentieth century, herpetologists, like most other kinds of zoologists, were concerned mainly with collecting and classifying new species and describing the anatomical structure of those which were already known. The study of fossil forms was also developed, and the discovery of remains of such huge and spectacular extinct reptiles as the dinosaurs seemed as exciting to the Victorian public as space-research does to us. As a result of this work the majority of the living species of reptiles were named and classified and, in outline at least, the wonderful history of the reptiles in past ages was pieced together.

Many modern herpetologists carry on these traditional studies on the classification and evolution of reptiles, but others have turned their attention to the life-histories of different species of reptiles, and the workings of the reptile body. Great progress has been made in the study of populations of reptiles in the wild, particularly with the aid of marking techniques (such as clipping scales) which enable released individuals to be recognised after recapture. In this way it has been possible to learn something about the growth and longevity of certain species, and the distances which individuals will travel. The social behaviour of reptiles has also been investigated, and it has been shown that many of them, particularly lizards, go through elaborate rituals of courtship and rivalry, comparable to those of birds. Several important recent studies of this kind, dealing with the life-history of various species, are listed in the Bibliography (p. 145).

In the laboratory much has been discovered about the reproduction of reptiles and the part played by the various glands, such as the testes, in controlling sexual behaviour and the onset of the breeding season. The roles of the various sense organs in such activities as mating and tracking prey have also been studied, while another important line of research is concerned with the ways in which reptiles regulate their body temperature.

In spite of the growth of these studies, a great deal remains to be learnt about even the commonest species of reptiles, and it is probably still true to say that less is known about the life of reptiles than that of any of the other groups of vertebrates. There is plenty of room for future workers of all kinds: for the non-professional who likes to keep reptiles, or who travels in hot countries where these animals are really plentiful; for the field naturalist who wants to study the behaviour of a lizard colony on an old wall; or for the laboratory worker who wishes to examine reptilian cells under the electron microscope. We shall feel particularly well rewarded if the following pages should encourage some of our readers to take up such studies, and thus add to man's knowledge of the reptile world.

Chapter 1

WHAT IS A REPTILE?

As most readers of this book will know, zoologists divide the Animal Kingdom into a number of compartments or 'pigeon holes' which enable the relationship of one animal to another to be clearly defined.* The major divisions are known as 'phyla' (singular 'phylum') from the Greek word *phulon*, meaning a 'tribe' or 'race'. Each phylum is divided into 'classes', each class into 'orders', each order into 'families', and each family into 'genera'; the various genera contain from one to many dozens of different kinds, or 'species', of animals. The arrangement is sometimes elaborated by the creation of extra divisions such as subphyla, superorders and suborders, superfamilies and subfamilies, and so on, to make the classification of the different animals still more flexible and exact.

The diagram on page 13 (Fig. 1) gives the main divisions into which the class Reptilia falls and shows the relationship between them. The best known extinct groups (plesiosaurs, ichthyosaurs, dinosaurs and pterosaurs) are shown, as well as the four living orders and the two sub-orders, the lizards and the snakes. The relationship of reptiles to amphibians, birds and mammals, is also indicated. A more detailed classification down to 'family' level is given in Appendix B on page 142.

The major division or phylum to which the class Reptilia belongs is the Chordata. This is nearly equivalent to the more popular term 'vertebrates' since it consists predominantly of animals with backbones. Every reptile—like

* The following brief account of the principles of classification is amplified in Appendix A, p. 140.

17

almost every fish, and every amphibian, bird and mammal—possesses the characteristic structure known as the vertebral column or 'spine'. This is composed of a number of jointed bones or cartilages, known as vertebrae, which surround and protect the spinal cord. The reptiles also share with all other vertebrates such structures as a skull, ears, eyes and nose, a heart and liver and many other organs such as we ourselves possess. In fact, a person knowing little of zoology might be very surprised to find how basically similar a reptile is to, say, a goldfish, a canary or a dog, and that the body of a snake is structurally much more like that of a man than that of an invertebrate such as a centipede or worm.

But although there is a basic anatomical likeness between a reptile and other vertebrates, there are also many important differences. It is these differences that distinguish reptiles from their vertebrate cousins which we shall first consider in this chapter. We shall then go on to deal with some of the characteristic reptile structures and organs, and give a simple explanation of how they work.

Some reptiles and amphibians are superficially very alike, and as recently as the early nineteenth century, naturalists made no distinction between the two groups. Even today many people would mistake a lizard for a salamander, or a snake for one of the burrowing limbless amphibians known as the Apoda, or 'legless ones'. There are, however, a number of ways of avoiding such a mistake, based partly on the evidence of external characters, and partly on the anatomy and life-histories of the two classes of animals.

For practical purposes, the most obvious difference between them lies in the skin. Present-day amphibians may have rough skins or smooth ones but they never have skins covered with scales (it is true that the Apoda do have scales, but these lie beneath the skin surface and are therefore not visible on the living animal). On the other hand, scales are highly characteristic of reptiles and are possessed in one form or another by every member of the group.

Another important difference lies in the mode of reproduction and the life-history of the two classes. Nearly all reptiles, whether they lay eggs or bear their young alive, reproduce on land; the young breathe air by means of lungs from the beginning, and their general appearance and mode of life is similar to that of their parents. Most amphibians, on the other hand, lay their eggs in water, and the young go through an aquatic larval stage as tadpoles when they breathe by means of gills. Some amphibians, it is true, do not conform with this rule and have evaded the necessity of breeding in the water in a variety of ingenious ways, but for the majority this remains a clear-cut distinction.

Confusion between reptiles on the one hand, and fish, birds or mammals on the other, is less likely than that between reptiles and amphibians, but nevertheless mistakes can be made. For instance, it would be quite easy to mistake a sea-snake for a snake-like fish such as an eel or a lamprey. Here again, however, the scales are a good practical guide, for in most snake-like fishes they are minute and inconspicuous. A more fundamental distinction is, of course, the universal presence of lungs in reptiles. Except for a few unusual genera, fish do not possess lungs; they breathe by means of gills and, if removed from the water, die sooner or later from asphyxiation.

No one would be likely to mistake a bird or a mammal of almost any kind for a reptile owing to their covering of feathers or fur. There are, however, a few scaly mammals such as the pangolins and armadillos which do have a rather reptilian appearance. It is therefore unfortunately impossible to frame some simple definition of a reptile as "an animal with lungs and scales" which will rule out every other kind of vertebrate. The more fundamental differences between reptiles and mammals are again related to their method of reproduction, and also to their physiology. With two exceptions (the echidna and duck-billed platypus) all mammals bring forth living young, and all of them nourish their offspring after birth from a supply of milk in the mother's body. Reptiles, on the other hand, often reproduce by means of laying eggs, and the mother plays no part in the direct nourishment of the young after birth or hatching. Both birds and mammals also have an elaborate physiological machinery which keeps their bodies at a fairly stable temperature, whereas the temperature of the reptile body fluctuates with the immediate environment. We shall have more to say about these interesting processes later on.

Zoologists know of many other criteria connected with the structure of the skeleton and internal organs which distinguish a reptile from other animal groups when its body is cut open. Some of these will be mentioned as we go along, but for a full treatment of the subject the reader must turn to a detailed textbook of zoology. Here we shall concentrate mainly on those aspects of reptile anatomy (or physical structure) and physiology (life processes) which are likely to be of general interest.

We may begin with a few remarks about the reptile's characteristic scales. These are formed from thickenings of the outer layer of skin, known as the epidermis (Fig. 2). They are composed of a hard substance known as keratin, which also forms part of the outer layer of the mammalian skin and is present in feathers, horns and hairs. The keratin itself is dead material and is continually being rubbed away and renewed from below by the deeper, living tissues of the epidermis. At least, this is what happens in crocodiles and tortoises; in lizards and snakes it is shed only at intervals —often several times a year—in large flakes or as a continuous slough. The numerous pigment cells are found mainly, though not exclusively, in the deepest region of the skin, known as the dermis; these are responsible for the coloration of the animal and play an important part in the phenomenon, shown by many reptiles, of colour change. In many reptiles, such as crocodiles and many lizards, there are small plates of bone known as osteoderms or osteoscutes (Fig. 2) in the dermal parts of the scales which make the

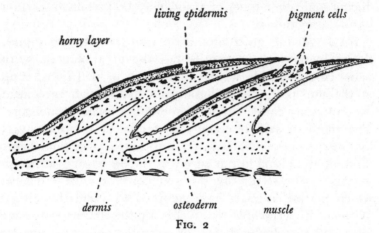

FIG. 2

Section through scales of lizard (e.g. slow-worm) showing epidermis and dermis and their pigment cells, and osteoderms.

skin exceedingly tough. In the head region these may become attached to the underlying skull bones.

The form and arrangement of the scales is very consistent in any given species, and to a lesser extent, within the bigger groups. This is particularly true of the big scales over the head which are often called shields. Consequently scales are much used as guides to identification, and their arrangement is often shown in the recognition keys and check-lists prepared by the experts, known as systematists, who specialise in the classification of animals (Fig. 25, p. 125).

People who know little of reptiles sometimes refer to them as 'nasty slimy creatures', but this judgment is quite untrue. Although the scales may be so smooth as to give the animal a shiny and perhaps a slimy appearance, the skin is, in fact, quite dry. It contains neither slime glands such as are found in fish and amphibians, nor sweat and grease glands such as are found in mammals. For the most part it is without glands of any kind, though a few scent-producing and other types of gland may be present in certain localised regions.

Besides giving good protection from mechanical injury, the scaly skin of the reptile has the great advantage of being comparatively waterproof. A reptile will not dry up in the sun as a frog is liable to do, although prolonged exposure may cause it to lose a certain amount of moisture. The reptilian skin is equally useful to those species that live in the oceans. Salt water can suck out the vital tissue fluids of an animal just as surely as the desert sun (although in this case waterproofing is only one of several devices which marine animals have adopted to avoid fluid loss). Without impermeable skins the reptiles might not have been able to colonise deserts or enter the sea, environments which are inhospitable to amphibians, perhaps partly because of their lack of effective waterproofing.

Turning now to the internal skeleton of reptiles, we find that like those of most other vertebrates, it consists of two materials, cartilage and bone. In the embryo the proportion of cartilage is very high, but as the young grow up much of this is converted into bone. In the adult the cartilage remains only in certain places, such as parts of the skull and shoulder-girdle and over the surfaces of the joints. The bones themselves are sometimes able to grow throughout the animal's life, although the rate of growth gets slower with age. This is one of the reasons why the adult size of individuals in some species of reptiles may vary more than it does in mammals, where bone growth ceases abruptly after a certain age.

The reptile skull (Fig. 3) contains a larger number of separate bones than that of mammals. It is jointed to (or 'articulates with' to use the proper technical expression) the first vertebra of the backbone by a single 'knob' (often partly divided into three lobes), known as a 'condyle'. This is similar to the arrangement found in birds, but differs from that found in modern amphibians and mammals, where there are always two condyles (Fig. 3c). Nearly all the vertebræ of reptiles, except the first one or two and those in the tail, may have well-developed ribs attached to them, whereas in mammals ribs are confined to the vertebræ of the chest region. In certain reptiles, such as crocodiles, the tuatara, and some lizards, there is also a series of thin, jointed bony rods in the substance of the belly wall which are known as abdominal ribs; these lie outside the true ribs and, being unattached to the main skeleton, may be lost in museum specimens.

The lower jaw of reptiles is made up of several bones firmly attached to each other. This is like the arrangement found in amphibians and birds, but differs from that found in mammals, whose lower jaws contain only a single bone, the mandible, on either side (Fig. 3b). Another anatomical likeness common to reptiles, birds and amphibians concerns the bony mechanism which conducts the vibrations produced by sound waves from the ear drum to the organ of hearing inside the skull. In all three classes this mechanism typically consists of a single bone known as the stapes, whereas in mammals there are two extra little conducting bones known as the malleus and the incus (Fig. 4, p. 26).

Little is known about the sense of hearing in reptiles, but in many of them it does not seem to be very important—at least in the generally understood sense of the perception of air-borne sounds. They are comparatively silent animals, their characteristic sound being a low hiss, and they lack the highly developed system of communication by different

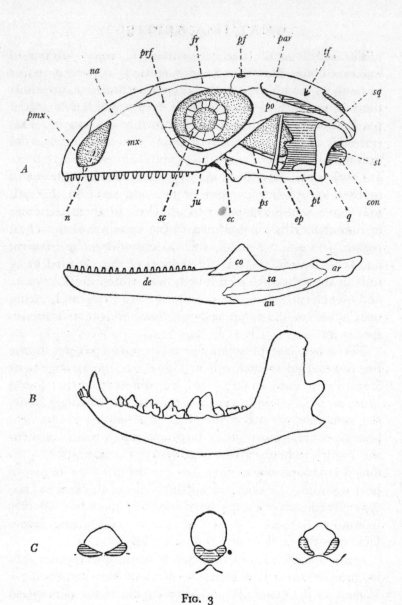

FIG. 3

A. Diagram of skull of lizard.

Only some of the more important bones are labelled, and their technical names have been used as in the great majority of cases there is no common equivalent. The regions shown in horizontal lines include the basisphenoid

24

noises and cries which is so evident in many birds and mammals. On the other hand it is probable that in some of them the ear plays an important part in detecting vibrations through the ground, while the apparent deafness of many others may merely be due to the fact that they do not respond in any obvious way to the sounds made by human beings.

Most reptiles have keen eyesight, although they are better at perceiving moving objects than stationary ones. Lizards and tortoises are known to have some ability to recognise colours. As a rule the fields of the two eyes overlap somewhat, giving a degree of binocular vision which is greatest in forms such as tree-snakes and chamæleons which need to be able to judge distances accurately in order to capture their prey.

Except in snakes, the eyeballs are stiffened by an investing coat of cartilage and often as well by a ring of small overlapping bones known as the 'scleral ossicles' (Fig. 3a, p. 24). The lower eyelid is the larger and more movable of the two (in mammals the opposite is the case) and there is

---

and occipital bones and the auditory capsule which surround the back parts of the brain. The stippled regions are mostly occupied by cartilage and membrane, which usually disappear in museum specimens.

The lower jaw consists of several bones, and the jaw joint is between the lower end of the quadrate (*q*) and the concave impression on the articular (*ar*). The ear drum lies behind the posterior concave face of the quadrate. The tip of the stapes (*st*) is shown in black. In some types of lizards the temporal fossa (*tf*) is roofed over by bone.

Abbreviations: *an*, angular. *ar*, articular. *co*, coronoid. *con*, occipital condyle. *de*, dentary. *ec*, ectopterygoid or transpalatine. *ep*, epipterygoid. *fr*, frontal. *ju*, jugal or zygomatic. *mx*, maxilla. *n*, opening for nostril. *na*, nasal. *par*, parietal. *pf*, pineal foramen. *pmx*, premaxilla. *po*, post-orbital. *prf*, prefrontal. *ps*, parasphenoid. *pt*, pterygoid. *q*, quadrate. *sa*, surangular. *sc*, scleral ossicles. *sq*, squamosal. *st*, stapes or columella auris. *tf*, temporal fossa.

B. Lower jaw bone or mandible of mammal (dog).

This corresponds with the dentary bone (*de*) of a reptile.

C. Occipital condyles (in horizontal lines) and foramen magnum (unshaded) of amphibian (frog) on left, mammal (hedgehog) on right, and reptile (iguana lizard) in middle.

The single condyle of this reptile is partly divided into three lobes; the condyles of the amphibian and mammal are paired.

usually a third eyelid, or 'nictitating membrane', which sweeps across the eye from front to back, wiping and moistening the transparent part of the eyeball, or cornea.

Smell is another important sense in many reptiles, especially in those which burrow and have only degenerate

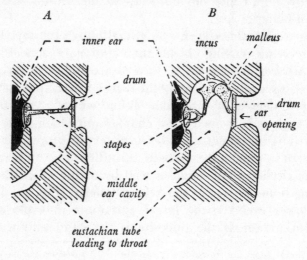

FIG. 4

Diagram showing arrangement of bones in the ear of reptile (*A*) and mammal (*B*). The diagrams are visualised as cross-sections through the side of the head. In *A*, the outer part of the stapes, in contact with the ear drum, is cartilaginous and known as the extra-stapes. Various processes, or projections from it are not shown.

eyes. In most of them a part of the nose becomes modified during embryonic life to form a special sense organ known as the organ of Jacobson (to be described on page 63). This is particularly well developed in lizards and snakes.

Even the most enthusiastic student of reptiles would not claim that they are intelligent animals. Their brains are small, both in absolute terms and relative to the size of their bodies, though as in other animals, the proportion of brain to body size tends to be higher in small species than in big ones. In many reptiles the brain weight is less than 0·5% of the total body weight; it is smaller still in a big reptile, such as an eight-foot crocodile, where the brain is only three to four inches long and under an inch across at its widest part. In fact reptiles normally have brains very little bigger than the brains of amphibians or fish of corresponding size.

In spite of the low brain-body ratio, however, the detailed structure of the reptile brain shows many resemblances to that of the much larger brains of birds. Moreover, it is interesting to note that the behaviour of reptiles and birds has certain features in common. In neither group is there as much capacity for learning or for adjustment to new situations as there is in mammals. There is, however, a tendency to develop elaborate patterns of instinctive or inborn behaviour associated with such activities as courtship and rivalry. This is very much more marked in birds, of course, but is still most clearly apparent in reptiles.

The teeth of reptiles usually have a simple pointed or peg-like shape and are not differentiated into incisors, canines and grinding or shearing cheek teeth as they are in mammals. On the whole they are more suitable for seizing and holding prey than for cutting it into pieces or chewing it. Reptiles, like fishes and amphibians, are not limited to two sets of teeth, the milk and permanent dentitions; most of them can go on losing and replacing their teeth as long as they live—a fact which may well give some members of our own species cause for envy.

As in other vertebrates, the alimentary tract of reptiles, which carries the food through the body from mouth to anus, is divided into several regions (Fig. 5), each with a different function. First comes the gullet or oesophagus, then the stomach and the small intestine where the process of digestion takes place, and next the large intestine, ending in the rectum, which carries away the undigested waste in the form of fæces. The hind end of the large intestine of

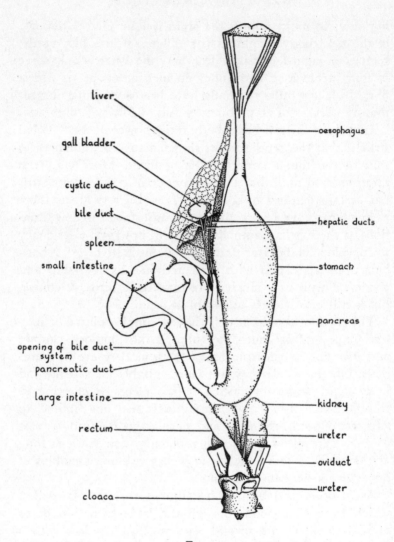

liver

gall bladder

cystic duct

bile duct

spleen

small intestine

opening of bile duct system

pancreatic duct

large intestine

rectum

cloaca

oesophagus

hepatic ducts

stomach

pancreas

kidney

ureter

oviduct

ureter

FIG. 5

Alimentary tract of common lizard (*Lacerta vivipara*).

The cystic duct, hepatic ducts and bile duct form a system carrying the digestive juice known as bile, which is produced by the liver, to the small intestine. Bladder not shown.

reptiles (as indeed of all classes of vertebrates except mammals) leads into a big chamber, the cloaca (the Latin for a sewer). This also receives the urine from the kidney ducts, or ureters, as well as the eggs or sperm from the ducts of the sex glands before they are expelled from the body. In crocodiles, the slit-like cloacal opening, or anus, is in line with the long axis of the body, but in lizards and snakes and in the tuatara it lies transversely (Fig. 21, p. 104).

In most reptiles the urine is excreted in the form of a substance known as uric acid which requires very little water for its elimination. This crystallises into a chalky white mass in the cloaca and is expelled, together with the fæces, in nearly solid form. The water required for the transport of the fæces and urine inside the body is mostly reabsorbed into the blood through the walls of the large intestine and cloacal chamber. This is an important method of water conservation, especially in reptiles which live in arid regions. In some reptiles there is a bladder opening off the cloaca in which the urine can be stored.

As we promised earlier in this chapter, we must now turn to the question of temperature regulation in reptiles as compared with other vertebrate groups. We have already mentioned that the body temperature of birds and mammals is maintained at a more or less constant level, despite the fact that it may get hotter or colder outside. The human body temperature, for example, is normally kept around 98·4° F. In reptiles, on the other hand, as in fishes and amphibians, the temperature tends to vary with that of the immediate surroundings. This is partly because they have no insulating coat of fur or feathers, or special cooling devices such as sweat glands. Birds and mammals are often called 'warm-blooded' and reptiles 'cold-blooded', but these terms are rather misleading, since in certain circumstances the temperature of a reptile may considerably exceed the normal temperature of man.

[Our ideas about the temperature of reptiles have been profoundly altered in recent years by the very interesting field and laboratory studies of Mr C. M. Bogert of the American Museum of Natural History, and his collaborators. They have shown that in the wild, reptiles are able to control their temperature to a considerable extent. The animals do not achieve this by conserving the warmth generated within their own bodies as mammals do, but by making use of external sources of heat such as the sun's rays or the heat of the sun-warmed earth. If they become cold they bask, and if they become overheated they move into the shade or take shelter underground. In many lizards the power of colour change provides a supplementary method of temperature control, for they can increase the amount of heat which they absorb by darkening their skins, and reduce it by growing pale. By such means reptiles are often able to keep their body temperature constant within a few degrees for quite long periods. Since they absorb heat from the sun or ground, their temperature may be well above that of the air.

Each species has its favourite temperature range—the one in which it functions most efficiently and seems to feel most comfortable. In many reptiles which live in hot countries this is well over 80° F., and in some desert lizards it may be as high as 100° (37–38° C.) or more; a few species are even active with a body temperature of over 107°. It is unlikely that our English reptiles would willingly tolerate body temperatures as high as this, for even a hot summer's day may be too warm for them to appear.

Such methods of temperature control are effective only if the weather conditions are warm and fairly stable, and if at the same time there is adequate shelter from excessive heat. Reptiles die easily from heat-stroke, and a rise in body temperature only a few degrees above that which they will voluntarily tolerate is often fatal. If they become too cold, on the other hand, their vital activities, such as the heart-beat and breathing, slow down and they are unable to remain active, to feed or to reproduce. Reptiles which live in regions where the climate fluctuates at all markedly are therefore active only for a part of the year, hibernating below ground in the winter, and in some cases æstivating during the hottest months of the year.

It is obvious that the temperature requirements of reptiles must have an important influence on their behaviour and choice of habitat. Many species are known to have a regular cycle of daily activity, emerging from their hiding places in the morning and basking until their temperatures reach the optimum level before embarking on the essential business of hunting and courtship. In the middle of the day they often retreat for a while, coming out again for a second period of activity in the late afternoon, and finally retiring as the temperature falls in the evening. The performance of such a routine demands the presence of suitable basking sites and shelter, and if these conditions are not satisfied, as often happens in captivity, the animals will only be able to live travesties of their normal lives.

Even during their periods of activity reptiles behave in a curiously spasmodic way, moving rapidly for a short distance and then relapsing into a phase of immobility. Generally speaking, they are incapable of sustained effort, at least by comparison with birds and mammals. This is partly because they have less control over the internal conditions of their bodies, such as temperature, the concentration of oxygen and other substances in their blood, and so on, than do the warm-blooded vertebrates. Also, their blood and respiratory systems are by avian and mammalian standards rather inefficient. For instance, the two chambers of the reptilian heart, known as the ventricles, are not (except in crocodiles) completely separated. For this reason, and also because of the arrangement of the great vessels which leave the heart, the arterial and venous bloodstreams mix so that the supply of oxygen to the tissues from the arterial blood is reduced. Their lungs, too, are less elaborately honeycombed, and therefore less effective as oxygenators, than those of mammals. They also lack the muscular diaphragm, which in mammals completely separates the thoracic and abdominal cavities and plays an important part in respiration.

Like many other animals, reptiles generally breed at a definite time during the year, although in certain tropical regions where the climate is very stable a few species may breed throughout most of the year. Even these, however show seasonal fluctuations in reproductive activity. In temperate and sub-tropical countries the animals usually mate in the spring and the young appear at the end of the summer; sometimes, however, there is a second mating period in the autumn.

The onset of mating, and the complicated activities such as rivalry and courtship which lead up to it, are evoked by hidden changes in the sex glands and other internal organs, such as the pituitary gland in the head. These are in turn influenced by changes in the environment, such as variations in temperature or humidity, or perhaps in the number of hours of daylight, or the food supply. The reproductive processes of reptiles seem particularly affected by outside influences of this kind, and it is not surprising that they so often fail to breed when the animals are kept under abnormal conditions in captivity.

Fertilisation in reptiles always takes place within the reproductive tract of the female, and not outside it as in most fish and many amphibians. To assist in this process the males in all reptiles except the tuatara have special organs of insemination which introduce the sperm into the cloaca of the female. In chelonians and crocodilians there is a single penis but in lizards and snakes there is a pair of these organs which are known as hemipenes (see p. 68). In some reptiles the sperm can live inside the female for a long time; this accounts for the occasional production of fertile eggs months or even years after the last mating.

The majority of reptiles reproduce by egg-laying and their eggs are always deposited on land, even when the adult spends nearly all its time in the water, as turtles do. They are usually concealed in some way, under stones or buried in the soil. As a rule the mother leaves them to be incubated by the warmth of their surroundings, a process which may take two months or more, but a few species show rather elementary forms of parental care. For example, female crocodiles guard their eggs and certain snakes and lizards brood them by curling round them (see also pp. 86, 110 and 138).

The eggs of reptiles are much like those of birds, though in some turtles, in snakes, and in most lizards, the shell is leathery instead of being hard and brittle. The colour varies from white to yellowish and the length from less than half an inch in the smaller species to three or four inches in big reptiles such as pythons and crocodiles. Some reptiles, such as geckos, lay only a couple of eggs at a time, whereas pythons, crocodiles and sea turtles may sometimes lay clutches of 50–100 or even more. All reptilian eggs contain a large quantity of yolk which provides the food they need for embryonic development, but they generally have to take up some water from their surroundings. The yolk is gradually used during embryonic life, but usually some is left over at the time of hatching, or, in the case of reptiles which produce their young alive (p. 36), at birth. In embryos near the end of their development this remaining yolk in its enclosing yolk-sac can be seen as a yellow blob attached to the body at the navel. In some species it is broken off when the little creature hatches or is born, but in others such as the adder and crocodile it is withdrawn

33

through the navel into the body. Here it provides a reserve of food during the first few months of post-natal life. The site of the navel persists for a while as a small scar on the belly, but eventually disappears.

Normally, of course, embryos do not develop unless the eggs inside the female are fertilised, but a new and most interesting possibility in reptilian reproduction has recently been described by two Russian workers, I. S. Darewski and W. N. Kulikowa, whose work is cited on page 146. They believe that certain populations of the lizard *Lacerta saxicola* in the Caucasus consist entirely of females and normally reproduce by the process of virgin birth or parthenogenesis. Further work should certainly be done on this, for the development under natural conditions of normal adult individuals from eggs which have never been fertilised by a male has not previously been proved to occur among higher vertebrates.

Within the egg the embryo develops special membranes known respectively as the amnion, the chorion and allantois (Fig. 6) to assist its survival. The amnion forms a kind of sac round the embryo and contains fluid which prevents it from drying up. This has caused it to be compared to a little private pool in which the unborn reptile can develop more safely than the amphibian tadpole in its public pond. The fused chorio-allantois, which is supplied with blood-vessels, lies close beneath the shell. It acts as an embryonic lung, and also as a receptacle for the waste products of excretion. These membranes are essential for the development of a land animal and are also found in birds and mammals.

There is a common belief that all reptiles lay eggs, but many lizards and snakes bear their young alive. At the moment of birth they may still be surrounded by their embryonic membranes, which form a kind of transparent 'egg', but they soon escape from them; sometimes they break out of the membranes while still inside the mother or during the birth process.

The embryonic development of such reptiles differs in certain important ways from that of mammals. In mammals (except for the platypus and the spiny anteater) the eggs are tiny and contain virtually no yolk. The developing embryos obtain their food, oxygen and other essentials

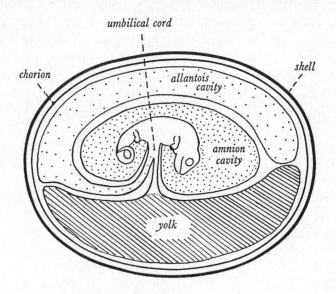

FIG. 6

Diagram showing in longitudinal section the general arrangement of embryonic membranes of an egg-laying reptile. In viviparous reptiles the shell is very thin or absent. The placenta, when present, is formed by parts of the chorion and allantois fused together, or of the chorion and yolk sac, which fit closely against the lining of the mother's oviduct.

from the mother's blood through an organ known as the placenta or 'afterbirth'. This is formed by the close union of the embryonic membranes with the lining of the mother's uterus. In live-bearing or viviparous reptiles, on the other hand, the eggs, although they have no shell or only a very thin one, are large and yolky like those of egg-laying or oviparous species. The embryos depend primarily on the

35

yolk for their sustenance and not, like embryo mammals, on the mother. This is shown by the fact that in the common lizard and probably certain other live-bearing species it is possible to remove the eggs from the mother's oviducts (the organs which correspond with the uterus) and incubate them in the laboratory. Broadly speaking it is true to say that the pregnant reptile merely acts as a kind of movable incubator for her eggs, retaining them inside her body until they are ready to hatch. This type of reproduction is often called ovoviviparity, to distinguish it from the different kind of viviparity found in mammals.

The situation is, however, more complicated than we have described. In some live-bearing reptiles—for example, certain skinks, snakes such as the adder, and some sea-snakes—the relationship between the mother and the embryos is more intimate, and a kind of placenta, comparable with that of mammals, is developed. In such species the placenta is probably important in helping water, oxygen and other gases to pass between the embryo and the mother. Its role in the nourishment of the embryo may often be only a supplementary one, the yolk remaining the principal source of food. In a few species, however, the yolk is quite small and the placenta may have an important nutritive function.

It is difficult to understand why some lizards and snakes should bear their young alive, while others, sometimes very closely related species, should be egg-layers. One can see, however, certain possible advantages in viviparity. Eggs retained inside the mother are probably better protected from enemies and from the weather, especially the hazards of drought and flooding, than those laid in a nest and abandoned. Furthermore, in uncertain climates the mother is able to make the best use of the available warmth to incubate her eggs by basking whenever the sun shows itself. This may well be one of the reasons why, of the few species of reptile which live in places where the climate is really cold, all, or nearly all, produce their young alive.

As in other creatures, embryonic development in reptiles may go wrong, and monstrosities such as double-headed snakes are sometimes found. Normally, however, the young hatch or are born as miniature replicas of their parents in almost all particulars except size, their ability to reproduce, and often colour.

When their incubation period is complete the young of egg-laying reptiles begin to attack the inside of the shell so that they can emerge into the world, and nature has equipped them with a special structure to help them in this task. In crocodiles, chelonians and the tuatara this is a horny knob on the end of the snout known as the egg-caruncle, similar to that found in birds. In lizards and snakes a sharp tooth, which is shed soon after hatching, projects from the tip of the upper jaw and serves the same purpose. This egg-tooth is also present in ovoviviparous species, but may be rudimentary.

With these few facts about the structure of reptiles, their differences from other animal groups, and the way in which they reproduce, we must conclude our first brief answer to the question 'What is a Reptile?'. It is, of course, a very incomplete answer, but we hope that the reader will find some of the gaps in his knowledge filled in as he reads through the following pages. Our intention is to introduce him to the four living orders of reptiles one by one, telling him something about the outstanding members of each. By thus meeting the individual animals, and learning something about the way they are made and live, he may perhaps come to share the authors' enthusiasm for the reptile group. Better still, we hope he may be encouraged to follow up his interest by consulting more detailed works, and also by direct study of the living animals in the vivarium or the field.

Chapter 2

TORTOISES AND TURTLES

TORTOISES appeal to the majority of people more than any other reptile. They have an amiable, slightly pathetic look which endears them even to those who find other kinds of reptiles repulsive. Children keep them as pets, they are given away as prizes at fairs, and their lumbering shapes are still a popular feature of many suburban gardens. Nevertheless, in spite of their familiarity, tortoises and their kindred are very odd creatures indeed. They have many unique peculiarities, both of structure and behaviour, which distinguish them from all other reptiles.

There is some confusion about the naming of tortoises and their allies which we must clear up before describing them in greater detail. All these animals belong to a single order, the Chelonia (see chart on p. 13), but there is no proper equivalent in English for this, and we are forced to use the scientific word 'chelonian' itself if we wish to refer in general to the members of the group. There are also a number of confusing differences in the naming of the various chelonians in different parts of the world. In England the name tortoise is applied to those kinds of chelonians which live on land, while marine chelonians are known as turtles. Freshwater chelonians are usually called terrapins, but sometimes water-tortoises or turtles. In America, however, chelonians of all kinds are often referred to as turtles. The word terrapin (which, incidentally, is of Red Indian origin) is also used in America for some of the smaller fresh-water forms.

Another point concerns the relation between the habitat of the different types of chelonians and their formal zoological classification. This classification is based on anatomical features, not on habitat, so it does not necessarily show whether a particular chelonian is a land-dwelling or water-dwelling form. In fact, inhabitants of the two different environments may sometimes be found in the same family: for instance, the family Testudinidæ (in some systems of classification, at least) contains not only the typical land tortoises but also the amphibious pond terrapins of the genus *Emys*.

The strangest, and also the most characteristic feature of a chelonian is its shell (Figs. 7, 8, pp. 40, 44). This consists of two parts, the carapace above and the plastron below, the two being connected by bridges between the front and hind legs on each side of the shell. The substance of the shell is built on a kind of two-ply principle. There is a thin outer layer of horny plates called laminæ, and a thicker inner one of bony plates, both layers being set in a regular pattern. On the carapace there is a single row of laminæ down the middle of the back, another row of larger ones on each side of this, and a series of small ones round the margins. The bony plates beneath the laminæ have a rather similar arrangement, but the edges of the laminæ and bony plates do not coincide; they overlap each other like the bricks of two successive courses in a wall. This prevents the shell from being weakened by the presence of 'double joints'. The plastron has a similar two-layered structure, but the laminæ and bony plates are less numerous and have a different pattern. The various laminæ and plates have individual names, and their arrangement is an important guide to the classification of these animals.

The laminæ correspond to the horny parts of ordinary reptilian scales and are likewise produced by a layer of living cells. These lie between the laminæ and the underlying layer of bony plates. As a chelonian gets bigger and older the laminæ increase in size by the addition of new

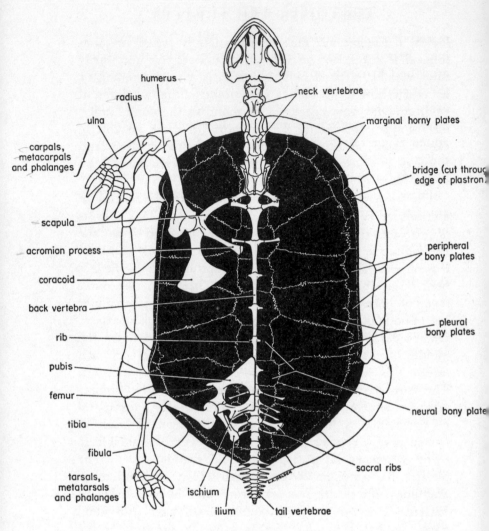

FIG. 7

Under surface of carapace and skeleton of tortoise (*Gopherus* sp.). The plastron has been removed and the limbs are shown on one side only.

The bony shell plates are shown in black, the outer, horny ones in white; they are named according to the system used by A. Carr (1952). The shoulder-girdle is made up of the scapula or shoulder blade, which has a long process called the acromion, and the coracoid. The humerus is the bone of the upper material beneath and around them. When the animals go into their prolonged seasonal sleep, or hibernation, this growth is arrested, and the dormant period is marked by the appearance of a line, forming a ring, round the previously formed material of each lamina. In species which have a regular hibernating season these rings are generally added at the rate of one a year, and can be compared with the rings seen on the scales of some fishes, and on the cut surface of a sectioned tree trunk. It should be possible to estimate the age of a tortoise by counting them, and in young animals a rough estimate can often be gained. Unfortunately, however, the method is not always reliable. Disease or food shortage may produce similar rings of arrested growth, and the surface of the lamina may be shed or rubbed away so that the older rings can no longer be seen.

The laminæ of some chelonians are put to commercial use by man, particularly those of the hawksbill turtle (*Eretmochelys*), which are used in the manufacture of the beautiful substance rather misleadingly known as 'tortoise-shell'. Unfortunately this can involve great cruelty to the animals, which are sometimes slowly roasted alive until the heat causes the laminæ to separate from the underlying shell bones. This method has been followed for many centuries in the Caribbean, and those who practise it justify its barbarity by saying that when the animals are set free afterwards a new, although perhaps imperfect, shell will grow in place of the old. In fact, however, no instance of such regeneration has been reliably recorded, and it seems unlikely that turtles misused in this way could live very long. It is perhaps just possible that regeneration could take

---

arm, the radius and ulna are the bones of the forearm, and the carpals, metacarpals and phalanges are the bones of the hand. The hip-girdle is made up of three bones, the ilium, ischium and pubis. The femur is the thigh bone, the tibia and fibula the bones of the leg, and the tarsals, metatarsals and phalanges the bones of the foot. The ribs of the back vertebræ are to a large extent fused with the shell, but the sacral ribs are separate structures.

place if the deeper growing layers of the skin were left intact, especially if only a few of the laminæ were skilfully removed. The subject of shell regeneration would well repay further study, confined, we may hope, to responsible laboratory techniques.

Unfortunately, we do not know exactly how or why chelonians developed their shells during the course of evolution. Nearly all the fossil remains of the oldest known types show that they were essentially similar to those living today, and there are only faint clues to their origin. In fact, chelonian ancestry suffers far more from 'missing links' than the ancestry of man.

But although we can say little or nothing about the origin of the chelonian shell we can at least describe some of the important ways it affects the living animal. Its main function is, of course, protective, and to that extent it is an aid to survival, but its rigidity has also imposed on its owner a number of special problems of adaptation. For instance, chelonians cannot breathe by expanding and contracting their chests as other reptiles do, for the simple reason that such movements are prevented by the plastron. Instead they have converted their belly muscles into a special breathing apparatus quite different from that found in other vertebrates. One set of these muscles widens the body cavity so that the lungs expand and draw in air, while another set presses the viscera against the lungs and causes the air to be expelled. Some freshwater chelonians are also able to breathe when submerged by sucking water in through the mouth and passing it over the membranes of the throat, which act as a kind of gill. In several species, such as the European pond terrapin (*Emys orbicularis*), there are thin-walled sacs opening off the cloaca which possibly function on the same principle, although in this case the water reaches them through the anus. Chelonians equipped in this way can stay under water for long periods, especially if they remain inactive and do not use up much oxygen. Some species can even hibernate for months at a time while submerged, though they may come up at intervals to breathe.

These special breathing arrangements are perhaps the most remarkable adaptations imposed on chelonians by their characteristic shell, but other anatomical specialisations arising from the same cause are worthy of mention. For instance, the shell removes the need for the long flexible backbone and the protective cage of ribs which characterise all other reptiles, and indeed vertebrates in general. The shell itself is quite sufficient protection for the vital organs within. We therefore find that the whole region of the back has shortened in chelonians, and that the vertebral column contains only about twelve individual bones apart from those in the neck and tail. Moreover, most of these are not freely articulated one with the other but are firmly attached to the under surface of the bony plates of the carapace (Fig. 8). Most of the ribs also have become fused with and partly merged into the shell, while the back muscles, which in other animals move the trunk from side to side, have become much reduced. In the neck and tail regions, however, where the chelonian body emerges from the shell, the spine can move very freely, and the surfaces of the joints between the neck vertebræ are highly modified to allow kinking when the head is drawn back within the shell.

Only two other special features dependent on the nature of the chelonian shell need be mentioned. First, the girdles of bone which serve as points of attachment for the limbs lie *inside* the ribs, and not outside as is the general rule in other vertebrates (Fig. 8). This very strange position is due to the ribs being pulled out over the girdles in the embryo by the outward growth of the carapace. Second, the breast-bone, or 'sternum', the collar-bone or 'clavicle', and another small bone usually present in reptiles called the 'interclavicle', are entirely absent. These bones are only necessary for an animal with a skeleton designed on comparatively flexible lines, and in the rigid, tank-like chelonians they have lost their function and, except for the sternum, seem to have become merged in the plastron.

Chelonians have many other interesting anatomical characteristics besides those which in some way or other

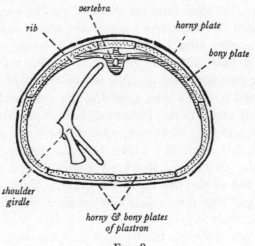

FIG. 8

Diagram of cross-section through middle of a tortoise showing the structure of the shell and the position of the shoulder girdle on one side (modified from Gadow, 1901).

are associated with the development of the shell. The structure of the skull, for example, is unlike that of other modern reptiles, and because of this chelonians are classified in the same major group, or subclass, as the most primitive and ancient reptiles of the geological past. Also, except for a few of the oldest fossil types, chelonians have no teeth. Instead they have developed a horny beak like that of birds on the upper and lower jaws. This can be used with only slight modification for dealing with almost any kind of diet: vegetation for land tortoises; invertebrates and fish for

1a. Matamata (*Chelys fimbriata*) from tropical South America.
1b. Baby Snapper (*Chelydra serpentina*) and egg.

2a. Giant Galapagos tortoise (*Testudo elephantopus ephippium*).

2b. Leatherback (*Dermochelys coriacea*) laying eggs. A Malay is catching the eggs as they fall.

3a. Thorny devils from Australia (*Moloch horridus*).
3b. Galapagos sea iguana (*Amblyrhynchus cristatus*).

4a. Tokay (*Gekko gecko*).

4b. Common iguana (*Ig
iguana*).

many terrapins; and a mixture of plant and animal food for sea turtles.

It is not always easy to tell the sex of a chelonian. The length of the tail is perhaps the best guide, for it is longer in the male, and thicker at the base where the penis is mounted. In some species the male also has enlarged claws on the fore-limbs which are used for grasping the female's shell, and his plastron tends to be concave so that the female's carapace can fit against it during the sexual act. There are often other sex differences, of course, such as size or colour, but these vary in each species and cannot be taken as a general guide.

The courtship of chelonians is a more animated affair than one might suppose. The details of procedure vary in different species and often include butting of the female by the male, and biting her on the head and feet. In some land tortoises, such as the giant *Testudo elephantopus* from the Galapagos, curious head-nodding gestures are made by the courting couple as they approach—a procedure, incidentally, which is also found in some lizards (see p. 70). Particularly elaborate forms of display are practised by some of the American painted and slider terrapins (*Chrysemys* and *Pseudemys*), where the male swims backwards in front of, or above the female, stroking her head with the very long claws of his front legs. In all the more thoroughly aquatic chelonians courtship and mating take place in the water.

During the act of copulation the male mounts the carapace of the female and inserts his penis beneath the back of it. He may rest his fore-legs on the front of the female's shell or grip it with his front claws, as sea-turtles do. In other species only the hind parts of the bodies of the pair come into contact, the male holding his body in a semi-upright position. Before and during the act the male often utters a variety of sounds, ranging from the roar made by giant tortoises to a high-pitched scream.

Chelonians, like crocodiles, always reproduce by laying eggs. The eggs of land tortoises and some terrapins have hard brittle shells, but in other terrapins and sea-turtles the shells have a parchment-like texture. The eggs are round or oval, and in the biggest chelonians, such as the giant tortoises and the leatherback turtle, may measure about two inches in maximal length. The number laid in a clutch varies from one in the African Tornier's tortoise (*Malacochersus tornieri*) to up to two hundred in big sea turtles, which may lay two or more clutches each year. The eggs are usually laid in holes dug in the ground by the female, who often moistens the earth with urine, perhaps making it easier to work.

The nesting of sea-turtles is particularly fascinating. The females come ashore, often at night, on remote sandy beaches and excavate craters in the sand above the high tide level with their paddles. Sometimes trial nests are dug and abandoned before the final laying site is selected. The eggs are finally covered over and well concealed before the female returns to the sea. The males often wait in the water off the shore while the females are on land.

The necessity of coming ashore to breed is the weak point in the turtle's life-history. The female, intent on laying her eggs, falls an easy prey to the hunter, while the young, which usually hatch after some two months' incubation, have many hazards to endure in the early hours of their life. They are attacked by birds as they cross the beach—their instinct seems to lead them downhill to the broad horizon of the sea—and by fishes when they enter the water. By no means all, or even most, of them survive to find the comparative safety of a coral reef or underwater jungle of weeds.

The living chelonians all belong to one of two suborders, distinguished from each other by the way the head is drawn into the shell and by the corresponding structure of the neck vertebræ. In one of these suborders, the Pleurodira or 'side-necks' the neck, as the name suggests, is bent sideways; in the other, the Cryptodira, or 'hidden-necks', it is bent up and down in the vertical plane.

The pleurodires or side-necked chelonians form quite a small group found in South America, Africa and Australasia. Apart from their peculiar method of withdrawing the head into the shell, and the fact that some of them have exceedingly long necks, most of these animals are not as striking as their cryptodire cousins. But the group does contain one outstanding curiosity in the matamata terrapin (*Chelys fimbriata*) of Brazil (Plate 1a). This remarkable creature is quite big, with a rough, ridged shell over a foot long. Its body is extremely flat, no doubt as an adaptation to living on the bottom. The wide, flat head is covered with filament-like excrescences, and there is a large ear-like flap of skin on each side behind the eyes. The front of the snout is drawn into a long slender proboscis with the nostrils at its tip, which can be thrust inconspicuously above the surface for breathing. The oddness of the creature's appearance is increased by the rather prominent chin and the set of the mouth which, as the American herpetologist Clifford H. Pope has said, gives the matamata a grinning or leering expression.

For long periods the animal lies sluggishly submerged, looking like a piece of waterlogged bark. It feeds on fishes and other small water animals which are engulfed in a rush of water when the terrapin suddenly opens its mouth. Possibly the prey are attracted by the movement of the appendages round its head, but this has not yet been definitely proved.

All the remaining terrapins, as well as the land tortoises and sea-turtles, are placed in the suborder Cryptodira. This is much the larger of the two groups, and contains some seven or more families as against two in the Pleurodira.

The exact numbers of families depend on the particular classification followed (see p. 142).

Of the cryptodire terrapins two are commonly sold as pets in Great Britain. These are the European pond terrapin (*Emys orbicularis*) and the red-eared terrapin (*Pseudemys scripta elegans*) of North America. In spite of their amphibious habits both these terrapins are grouped by some workers with the typical land tortoises in the great family Testudinidæ.

A full-grown European pond terrapin has a shell about seven inches long. This is usually dark brown with yellow dots which show up best when the animal has just left the water. There is a slightly flexible hinge across the middle of the plastron, which is connected with the carapace only by fibrous tissue instead of a firm bony bridge. The creature is found in countries along both sides of the Mediterranean, and further north in France, Germany and Poland. Fossil remains of quite recent members of the species have been discovered in the Norfolk fens. It is the most northerly ranging of all chelonians and can be kept out of doors in a suitable enclosure in this country, at least during the summer. A related species, *Emys blandingii*, lives in North America.

The pond terrapin is almost entirely carnivorous, subsisting mainly on insects, molluscs, and frogs and their tadpoles. It will eat small fish, and even ducklings when it can catch them, and sometimes forages on land for slugs and snails. Any food caught on land will be carried back to the water, where all terrapins prefer to feed. The pond terrapin is a messy eater. It tears its prey to pieces with its front claws, and in captivity soon fouls its tank so that frequent changes of water are necessary.

A particularly good account of the habits of this terrapin is given by the well-known French naturalist Raymond Rollinat in the book listed on page 148. One interesting fact that Rollinat noted was that some of his captive specimens would hibernate on land in heaps of manure. In the wild state, however, the animals probably spend the winter in mud at the bottom of the pond or in holes in the bank.

The red-eared terrapin and some of its relatives are among the most brightly coloured of all chelonians, and the attractive babies, with shells little bigger than a half-crown are often seen in pet shops. Unless they are treated with special care, however, not many will survive long in captivity. These terrapins have a bright red band behind the eye, and the head, limbs and tail are striped with yellow. The shell also has yellow markings, while in the painted terrapin (*Chrysemys picta*), the edges of the carapace are ornamented with red. Luckily these pretty creatures are not too difficult to keep when grown up.

There are many other kinds of terrapins in the family Testudinidæ, mostly of small or medium size. The map and diamondback terrapins *Graptemys* and *Malaclemys* are typical examples, the last-named being much sought after as a delicacy by American gourmets. A few related forms grow to a much larger size than the average terrapin; for instance, the herbivorous genus *Batagur* from south-eastern Asia has a shell nearly two feet long.

The box terrapins (*Terrapene*) are also found in North America and are in some ways intermediate between the pond terrapins and the land tortoises. Like the latter they have high, domed shells, live mainly on land, and eat some vegetable food. These terrapins owe their name to the characteristic design of the plastron, which has a well-developed hinge midway across its length (Fig. 9a). This enables the two halves to be pressed together very tightly against the cara-pace, completely enclosing the head and extremities. One species of box terrapin, known as *Terrapene carolina*, has been proved to have the exceptional length of life commonly associated with chelonians. Authentic records of the age of this animal show that it may have a life-span of over 60 years.

Another family of terrapins called the Chelydridæ (a name derived, rather misleadingly, from the Greek *chelydros*, a water-serpent) includes the mud and musk terrapins and the snappers. This is an all-American group containing many interesting members. The common snapper (*Chelydra*

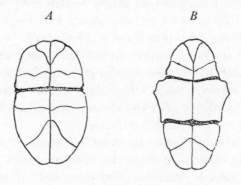

FIG. 9

Plastra of (*A*) box terrapin (*Terrapene carolina carolina*) and (*B*) mud terrapin (*Kinosternon dunni*) showing position of hinges (stippled). (After H. Wermuth and R. Mertens, *Schildkröten Krokodile Brückenechsen*, Gustav Fischer, Jena, 1961).

serpentina; Plate 1b) is renowned for its truculence, biting fiercely when molested and striking with its jaws like a snake. It is a large, ugly creature reaching a weight of over 50 lbs., with a very big head and hooked beak, a long tail and thick strong claws. The head cannot be withdrawn beneath the carapace, and the plastron is small so that the neck, tail and legs are widely exposed on the under surface.

The snapper is well equipped for predatory life, and captures fish and waterfowl by stalking them beneath the water or lying in ambush. It does not seem, however, to be so destructive to water life as one might expect, and recent surveys, based on examination of the stomach contents of large numbers of individuals, suggest that it eats almost as much plant as animal food.

The common snapper has a much bigger relative known as the alligator snapper (*Macrochelys temminckii*) which reaches a weight of at least 200 lbs. and is mainly restricted to the south-eastern parts of the United States. In habits and appearance it is much like *Chelydra*, but the three keels along the top of its carapace are more pronounced than in its smaller relation. This terrapin also has a curious forked structure rising from the floor of the mouth which can become pink in colour and be moved about in a worm-like manner. Observations on young specimens in aquaria have shown that this is definitely used as a lure to attract small fishes into the gaping jaws as the terrapin lies motionless at the bottom.

Although the truculence of this formidable chelonian is well established it seems that estimates of its biting power may have been exaggerated. After reading in the older natural history books that a full-grown alligator snapper can bite through a broomstick, it is disappointing to learn from recent observations (Carr, 1952) that a forty-pound specimen can hardly sever a pencil.

The mud terrapins (*Kinosternon*) and the musk terrapins (*Sternotherus*) are probably related to the snappers and are sometimes included in the same family. The musk terrapins— or 'stink pot' terrapins to give them their more evocative name—are noted for the unpleasant smell which they can produce from scent glands in their flanks whenever they are annoyed. Both mud and musk terrapins have hinged plastra, though the hinges are much more flexible in the former group. They differ, however, from the European pond terrapin and the box terrapins in having two transverse hinges instead of one (Fig. 9b). The plastron is thus divided into three segments, of which the middle one is fixed. These different but comparable arrangements suggest that a hinged shell of one sort or other has been independently developed by several different groups of chelonians during the course of evolution.

One of the most interesting of the main groups of fresh-water chelonians is the family of soft-shelled turtles (*Trionychidæ*), found in America, Africa and the East (Fig. 10). These are highly adapted for life at the bottom, and their flat, rounded shells show a drastic reduction in armour. There are no horny laminæ and the bony plates are simply covered by leathery skin. The plates themselves are absent round the rim of the carapace, and there is no firm union between this and the plastron. The latter is even less complete, and there are large areas of non-bony tissue between the various plates. The head, however, can be very completely retracted, and in some genera, notably the Indian pond terrapins (*Lissemys*), the hind leg openings can be closed by movable flaps of skin. The chelonians of this family seem to be particularly prone to a curious hump-back deformity which produces a large and often asymmetrical bulge on the normally flat shell. This is occasionally seen in other chelonians and is due to some disharmony of growth between the backbone and the bony plates of the carapace.

Although they can if they wish swim very fast with sweeps of their webbed, three-clawed feet, soft-shelled terrapins spend long periods buried in the mud or shingle of the bottom. Here their pancake-like shells, which in some species have a spotted or stippled pattern, harmonise very well with their surroundings. Their nostrils are set at the end of a tubular proboscis rather like that of the matamata, which can be thrust out of the mud, or above the surface if they are in shallow water. They seem to rely more on underwater breathing than other terrapins, and in some species at least there are special filaments on the lining of the throat which have a gill-like function.

These terrapins eat a certain amount of plant food, but are mainly carnivorous, catching crustaceans and fishes with lightning darts of their long necks as they lie in muddy ambush. Their jaws, concealed by fleshy lips, are very strong and the bigger species can inflict serious bites. Some of the Old World species in the family grow very big indeed, having shells over a yard long.

Like many other reptiles, terrapins have aroused strong and mixed emotions in the minds of men. In parts of Africa

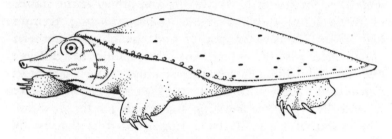

FIG. 10

Soft-shelled turtle (*Trionyx spiniferus*, a North American species). (Adapted from photo by P. Pritchard.)

and the East they are highly esteemed as food. On the other hand some species are venerated by Hindus, Muslims and Buddhists, and are kept in special tanks attached to temples and shrines.

Terrapins, as we have seen, are mainly aquatic animals adapted to life in fresh water. Although they may have such special adaptations to a water-dwelling life as webbed feet many species also make numerous excursions ashore, not only to lay their eggs, but also in search of food. When we turn to marine turtles, however, we find that they have carried their aquatic adaptations much further. The limbs of all species are converted into paddles, which enable them to swim with greater agility, and on land their movements are very laborious. In fact they only leave the water to breed (and then only the females come ashore) and perhaps occasionally to bask on a sandbank. Although the horny laminæ of their shells are well developed, the bony plates are reduced, probably to increase their buoyancy, and there may be gaps between the ends of the ribs where the bone has disappeared.

All but one of the different kinds of marine turtles belong to the family Cheloniidæ, and this contains only four genera and about five species. These are the green turtle (*Chelonia mydas*), popular with Lord Mayors and others as the source of turtle soup; the loggerhead (*Caretta caretta*); Kemp's loggerhead (*Lepidochelys kempi*), and the olive loggerhead (*Lepidochelys olivacea*), which are often known as 'ridleys'; and the hawksbill (*Eretmochelys imbricata*). The loggerhead *Caretta* and the green turtle are the biggest of these and may have shells over three feet long and weigh 300 lbs. or more. The hawksbill can easily be distinguished from the rest by the overlapping arrangement of the laminæ of the carapace, and the serrations along the hind parts of its edges.

In their general habits these turtles are much alike, though the loggerhead is more carnivorous in its diet than the other species. Most of them have a very wide distribution throughout the warmer seas, and northerly wanderers quite often cross the Atlantic in the Gulf Stream and become stranded in the British Isles. It is probable that in some places turtles make regular migrations related to breeding and climatic changes, and Professor Carr and his colleagues have made some interesting studies on the recovery of turtles marked by attaching metal tags to the shell or paddles. Green turtles which were marked on Ascension Island in the South Atlantic have been recovered near Brazil, 1,400 miles away. Professor Carr is reported to be trying out a new method of tracing the wanderings of turtles by radio, using small transmitters which can be attached to the shell and come into action when the animal surfaces to breathe every half minute or so. Such methods may well clear up many problems of the mysterious life-history of these interesting and economically important creatures.

The most remarkable of all marine turtles is the leather-back, *Dermochelys coriacea* (Plate 2b). It is the biggest of all living chelonians and one of the largest living reptiles, occasionally reaching a weight of over 1,000 lbs. and a shell length of over 6 feet. It is also the most perfectly adapted of the turtles for aquatic life, swimming with tremendous speed and sometimes seeming almost to fly through the water with sweeps of its very long, wing-like front paddles. It ranges far and wide throughout the warmer seas, but is nowhere very common except off the coast of Ceylon. Like most other turtles it is more or less omnivorous, feeding on seaweed, invertebrates and fish.

Unfortunately, the world's population of leathery turtles is seriously threatened by the demand for the eggs as human food, and many former breeding sites in Ceylon and the Caribbean have been wiped out. Luckily, strenuous efforts at conservation are being made in Malaya, where large numbers of eggs are being collected for safe keeping, so that the young can be liberated. In a recent book listed on page 147, J. J. Parsons describes similar methods for the conservation of the green turtle.

In young leatherbacks the body and paddles are covered by scales, but these are soon lost, leaving a surface of black leathery skin. As in the soft-shelled terrapins this is devoid of horny laminæ. Beneath the skin on the back is an extraordinary kind of carapace made up of a very large number of small bony plates. These fit together like the tiles of a mosaic, and are raised at intervals to form seven ridges which run the length of the back. The bony plates found in the carapace of other chelonians are absent, except for a single bone at the back of the neck. On the belly there is no complete mosaic, but several separate longitudinal rows of platelets and a ring of slender bones which correspond with the outer parts of the plastron of other turtles. The ribs and vertebræ of the animal are not, as in other chelonians, fused with this curious shell, so the skeleton approximates more closely to the 'normal' vertebrate appearance.

There has been a great deal of discussion as to whether the armour of the leatherback is what scientists call 'primitive' or 'specialised'. In other words, is it possible that the creature never developed a proper shell and so remains a primitive form? Or did its ancestors once have a shell which they later lost as a new specialised adaptation? Modern opinion inclines to the latter view, with the proviso that the unique mosaic of bony platelets may perhaps be a special development peculiar to *Dermochelys* and its fossil relatives. Whatever ideas on the problem are accepted, it is generally agreed that the leatherback is sufficiently distinct from the other sea-turtles to deserve at least a family of its own, the Dermochelyidæ.

Our last group of chelonians, the land tortoises, all belong to the family Testudinidæ, most of them to the genus *Testudo*. This word, the Latin for tortoise, was also applied by the Romans to a kind of military formation in which soldiers storming a fortress advanced under cover of their shields. These were held in such a way that the edges of each man's shield touched those of his neighbours, like the laminæ of the chelonian carapace, presenting an oblique armoured surface against the defenders' missiles.

In nearly all land tortoises the shell is high and domed, its shape giving good protection against the jaws of an aggressor. The laminæ are tough and strong, but in some of the giant types the bony plates are very thin, perhaps to cut down weight. Some species have hinged plastra, and in one genus, *Kinixys*, a part of the carapace is movable.

The curious African tortoise *Malacochersus tornieri* is remarkable in having a very thin flat, flexible shell so that the animal can wedge itself firmly between rocks when it inflates its body with air. In a few species the shell is very attractively marked. For instance, the starred tortoise, *Testudo elegans*, of southern India, has a yellow star-like pattern on each carapace lamina. One sometimes sees these shells mounted in silver and made into snuff-boxes.

Tortoises are found in a variety of habitats, from forests to open grass-lands and rocky country. Some such as the American desert tortoise (*Gopherus agassizii*) are inhabitants of the desert and dig burrows in which they shelter from extremes of heat or cold. The European species live mainly in dry places, such as wooded or scrubby hillsides.

The tortoise most often sold in this country is *Testudo græca*, common in southern Europe and north Africa. It can be distinguished from its relatives by the presence of a horny spur on the back of each thigh. Unfortunately there has been some confusion over the naming of these European tortoises, since *Testudo græca* has been called *Testudo ibera* by some workers, and the name *græca* has also been used for the species now generally known as *Testudo hermanni*. A third species, *Testudo marginata*, actually deserves the name 'Greek tortoise' better than either of the others, for it is common in Greece and occurs almost nowhere else.

These small tortoises do quite well out of doors in an English garden, though they very seldom manage to breed. They may hibernate successfully out of doors, buried in the ground, but it is safest to put them in a box in a cool out-house during the winter. Like other land tortoises they normally feed on grasses, berries and other plants, and pets allowed to roam the garden may exasperate keen gardeners and housewives by making inroads upon lettuce and strawberry beds. In captivity they may sometimes take animal food. Readers wishing for good advice on the keeping of tortoises should consult the helpful little book by I. and A. Nöel-Hume, cited on page 147.

A brief reference has already been made to the longevity of chelonians, which has become proverbial, and there can be no doubt that some of the land tortoises can live to a great age if they are lucky enough to escape death from disease or accident. For example, apparently reliable figures of over 100 years are quoted for *Testudo græca* and of 152 years for one of the giant Indian Ocean species. It is possible that the animals have a very much longer potential life-span than this, but authentic records going back so far are very hard to obtain.

In size land tortoises range from a shell length of six inches or so to giants with shells up to four feet long. Some of the fossil types are considerably bigger even than this. Several quite large land tortoises with shells of up to two feet long still live on the mainland of South America and Africa, but in recent times all the true giants have been restricted to three groups of tropical islands. These are the Galapagos Islands (the name means tortoise in Spanish) in the eastern Pacific, and the Mascarene and Aldabra Islands in the Indian Ocean around Madagascar. Vast numbers of the animals once lived unmolested on these islands, but they were soon discovered by the early navigators, who found them a valuable source of fresh meat which could be transported alive on board ship and slaughtered as required. By the early part of the nineteenth century the giant tortoises of Mauritius and the other Mascarene Islands had been exterminated like their compatriots the dodo and solitaire. Today only the Aldabra tortoises (*Testudo gigantea*) and some races of the Galapagos species (*T. elephantopus*; Plate 2a) survive. The Aldabra tortoises are said to be quite plentiful, but the Galapagos forms are seriously threatened.

The spectacle of giant tortoises has often aroused wonder

and curiosity in thoughtful minds. The young Charles Darwin who visited the Galapagos in 1835 as naturalist on board the 10-gun survey brig *H.M.S. Beagle*, was much impressed by them, and his reflections on the effects of geographical isolation on the tortoises and other inhabitants of this remote volcanic archipelago were later to form an important link in the chain of evidence for his theory of evolution.

Herman Melville, the great American writer, has left a more fanciful account of the giant tortoises in his delightful sketch, *The Encantadas; or Enchanted Isles*, and quotes a mariner's superstition that "all wicked sea-officers, more especially commodores and captains, are at death (and, in some cases, before death) transformed into tortoises" and left to dwell in these wastes, "solitary lords of Asphaltum."

With this whimsical thought in mind we must conclude our description of some of the living chelonians of the world. Much has necessarily been omitted, but we have perhaps managed to suggest that no one who is interested in chelonians need restrict his observations to the pet terrapin in the vivarium or the lumbering tortoise on the garden lawn. These are only two members of a widespread order of animals which will well repay the study of the curious herpetologist who wishes to broaden his understanding of the natural world.

Chapter 3

LIZARDS AND THE TUATARA

THE lizards are the most abundant, versatile and by far the most conspicuous of modern reptiles. A man might live for a year in the tropics without seeing a snake, but on his first evening in an hotel, if it were not too modern and hygienic, the geckos would come out from their lairs behind the furniture and chase insects across the ceiling.

To the casual eye many lizards may seem much alike— small four-legged reptiles with long tails, which bask in the sun and dart swiftly away when disturbed. There are many other kinds, however, such as the limbless slow-worm, which do not fit this picture at all. When one gets to know more about lizards one is impressed by the extent to which the different kinds vary in appearance and habits, and by the remarkable and diverse adaptations they show to different ways of life.

In hot countries there is hardly any place where lizards are not found, whether it be a rubble-piled building site in a great city, a dense rain-forest or the sandy wastes of the desert. Like other reptiles, lizards become less common and varied in temperate countries, but a few manage to exist even in places where the climate is really severe. The common English lizard, *Lacerta vivipara*, is found in Lapland just north of the Arctic Circle, and at the southern extreme of latitude the range of one genus of the iguanid family, extends right down to the tip of South America, including the desolate land of Tierra del Fuego. This genus may also hold the record for altitude, for one of its species is found at a height of over 15,000 feet in the Peruvian Andes.

Before introducing the different kinds of lizards, we must

5a. Frilled lizard (*Chlamydosaurus kingi*).
5b. Chamaeleon (*Chamaeleo dilepis*) with tongue extended.

6a. Anole lizard (*Anolis capito*) with throat-fan extended.

6b. Girdle-tailed lizard (*Cordylus giganteus*).

7a. Spiny-tailed skink (*Egernia stokesi*).
7b. Very young slow-worms (*Anguis fragilis*).

8a. Young Nile monitor (*Varanus niloticus*) with tail ready to strike.

8b. Mexican heloderm (*Heloderma horridum*).

briefly describe the lizard body and how it works. The skull (Fig. 3, p. 24) is lightly built and usually has big openings for the jaw muscles in its sides, behind the eye sockets or orbits. The quadrate bone, to which the lower jaw is hinged, is usually movable, and the whole of the upper jaw and the front part of the skull can also move slightly on the back part. Such movement is known as 'cranial kinesis', and is also found in birds and certain other reptiles, though not in chelonians and crocodilians. Its function is probably to increase the gape a little as struggling prey is being swallowed, and to help in shifting it round in the mouth. It has also been suggested that it provides a kind of shock-absorber effect when the jaws are snapped together against a resistance.

The teeth of lizards are particularly interesting. All living species have teeth on the bones round the edges of the jaws, but some also have them on the roof of the mouth on the bones known as the pterygoids, and very occasionally, on the palatines. In many lizards the teeth are cone-shaped, or blunt and peg-like (see Fig. 3); in others, such as the slow-worm and most monitors, they are sharp and curved slightly backwards (Fig. 11c). A few lizards such as certain agamas have big teeth, rather like the canines of mammals, near the front of the upper and lower jaw, while in certain iguanas the teeth towards the back of the jaws have their crowns divided into several lobes, or are serrated at their edges (Fig. 11d). These variations are not as obviously related to the type of diet as they are in mammals, and the majority of lizards seem to feed more or less indiscriminately on insects, worms and other small creatures, irrespective of the nature of their teeth.

The way in which the teeth are attached to the jaw bones is of some importance in classification. In the majority of lizards, including such groups as the iguanas, lacertids and monitors, they are attached to the inner side of the jaw bone so that their bases are oblique; this condition is known as 'pleurodont' (Fig. 11a). In some other types, however, such as the agamids and chamæleons (and also in the tuatara,

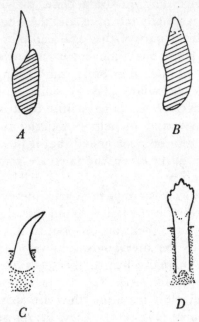

A   *B*

C   *D*

FIG. 11

Teeth of lizards.

A, B. Diagrams showing (*A*) pleurodont method of tooth attachment found in most lizards (e.g. monitors), and (*B*) acrodont method characteristic of agamids and chamæleons. The lower jaw (slanting lines) is shown in cross section with its outer side to the right.

C, D. Teeth at side of right lower jaw in (*C*) slow-worm and (*D*) *Iguana* sp., seen from inner surface.

which though not a lizard resembles one in many respects) they are set squarely on the jaw, in the manner known as 'acrodont' (Fig. 11b). Lizards with acrodont teeth do not seem able to replace them throughout life in the usual reptilian way, and in the tuatara the teeth are hardly replaced after hatching, and become very worn in old specimens.

The tongue varies greatly in shape. In the monitors (Fig.

12c) and the tegus it is long, slender and deeply forked, and can be withdrawn, as in snakes, into a kind of sheath; in others, such as the lacertids and the slow-worm (Fig. 12b), it is shorter and broader and forked only towards the tip; in others again, such as the agamas and the geckos, it is broad and fleshy, and the tip is blunt or only slightly notched (Fig. 12a).

In addition to its functions of taste and touch and, in some

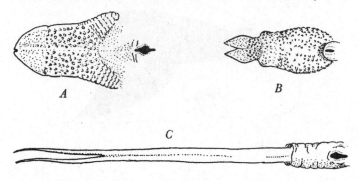

FIG. 12

Tongues of lizards. The glottis (opening of the windpipe) is shown in black.

A, *Gekko gecko*. *B*, slow-worm (*Anguis fragilis*). *C*, *Varanus monitor*. (After Malcolm Smith, 1935, *The Fauna of British India, Sauria,* Taylor and Francis, London; and 1954, cited on p.148).

lizards, of seizing prey or manipulating it in the mouth, the tongue also works in conjunction with a pair of interesting sense organs known as the organs of Jacobson (Fig. 13: see also p. 26). These are also present in chelonians and the tuatara, as well as in most mammals, but in lizards and snakes they are particularly large and elaborate. Each organ is shaped like a hollow dome, lying above the roof of the mouth and communicating with it through a narrow duct which opens near the front of the palate, a little to one side of the mid-line. The sense served by these organs undoubtedly resembles smell, for they are partly lined with a sensitive

63

membrane similar to that of the nose; they are also supplied by what is, in effect, a separate branch of the nerve of smell. What seems to happen is that minute particles are picked up by the tongue tips from the air or ground and carried by them into the organs of Jacobson (or at least to the openings of their ducts), to be 'smelt' by the sensitive cells lining their

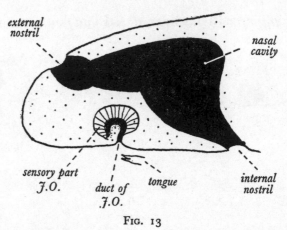

external nostril

nasal cavity

sensory part J.O.

duct of J.O.

tongue

internal nostril

FIG. 13

Diagram of longitudinal section through snout of lizard showing Jacobson's organ (J.O.), tongue tip and nasal cavity.

cavities. This is the explanation for the constant flickering of the tongue which is seen in a prowling snake or monitor lizard. It seems certain that the organs of Jacobson play an important part in such activities as trailing prey, testing food, sex recognition and courtship, either when used by themselves, or in conjunction with the sense of smell proper. These organs, like the smell-sensitive parts of the nose, tend to be reduced in tree-living lizards such as anoles (p. 77), which hunt almost entirely by sight. In the chamæleons the organs of Jacobson are rudimentary.

In many lizards the eyelids show interesting modifications (Fig. 14). In some skinks and certain other types, for example, the lower eyelid contains a transparent window so that the lizard can close its eyes to keep out sand and grit, while yet being able to see. In others this trend has apparently been carried still further, and both the upper and lower eyelids have become transparent and fused together. By this adaptation, which is also found in snakes, a kind of permanent spectacle is formed over the cornea. As one might expect, such modifications are often found in lizards that live in earth

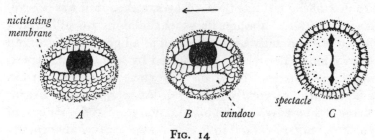

FIG. 14

Eye-coverings of lizards. Arrow points forwards to nose.

A, typical condition with upper and lower lids and nictitating membrane. *B*, with window in lower lid, as found in certain skinks, etc. *C*, condition seen in many geckos, with spectacle instead of lids, and slit pupils with serrated margins.

or sand but they are also found in geckos, many of which are climbers.

In burrowing lizards the eyes are reduced, sometimes to tiny vestiges, and the ear-drums are also small or absent. It is easy to understand that such creatures do not need acute hearing, but loss of the ear-drums has also occurred in certain agamids, in chamæleons and some other tree lizards which might be expected to need their ears. This seems to be another puzzling anomaly, like the spectacle of climbing geckos. Such examples show that it is not always possible to see an obvious connection between structural modification and the habits of an animal.

Both the tuatara and many lizards have a well developed 'third eye', often called the parietal or pineal eye, which lies on the top of the head in the mid-line, just beneath a hole near the front of the parietal bone (Fig. 3, p. 24). The skin over this is modified and less pigmented than the neighbour-ing skin. In other kinds of living reptiles the parietal eye is rudimentary or absent, but if the presence of the hole in the skull roof is any guide it seems to have been present in many fossil reptiles and amphibians.

The microscopic structure of the 'third eye' looks rather like that of the ordinary paired eyes, although it has no eye-lids or muscles. Although its exact functions are still myste-rious it has generally been regarded as a light-sensitive organ of some kind. This view is supported by some recent experi-ments in America in which the parietal eye of certain iguanids was surgically removed. As a result the lizards exposed themselves more to the sun than did animals in which the organ was left intact, and also became abnormally restless. Such experiments suggest that the 'third eye' acts as a kind of register of solar radiation, and helps to regulate the animal's exposure to sunlight. We have seen that basking is the principal way in which reptiles maintain their body temperatures at levels required to keep them active. It is possible, therefore that the parietal eye is ultimately import-ant in influencing the extent of the animal's overall activity— in a sense, the intensity of its life.

Although most lizards possess four limbs with five fingers or toes on each, a considerable number have lost or dras-tically reduced their legs and have become so snake-like that it is not easy to tell the two kinds of reptiles apart (see p. 103). In some lizards the fore-limbs are more reduced than the hind-limbs, while in others the reverse is the case. In others again, both pairs are equally degenerate. Although in such lizards as the slow-worm there may be no external trace of limbs, the skeletal structures known as limb girdles are seldom, if ever, completely lost, and vestiges of them can be revealed beneath the skin by careful dissection or X-rays.

Limbless lizards differ from snakes in this respect, which generally show no skeletal evidence that they once had legs. Another difference between the two types of reptiles is related to their choice of environment. Nearly all the limbless or nearly limbless lizards are either burrowers or live near the ground, under stones and logs, or among the roots of plants. Many kinds of snakes, on the other hand, are well adapted to arboreal life.

The tendency to lose the limbs is seen in nearly half of the eighteen or so families of lizards. Sometimes it occurs in all the members of a family, sometimes only in a few. It may seem strange that lizards with well-developed legs such as the alligator lizards (p. 88) should be placed in the same family as limbless creatures like the slow-worm; but we know from detailed studies of lizard anatomy that the state of the limb is not necessarily a reliable guide to family, or even generic relationship. In the skinks, for example, it is possible to find a whole series of related species which show all degrees of limb reduction; at one extreme all four legs are well developed, and at the other there are no external traces of limbs at all (p. 85).

As most people know, a large number of lizards, as well as the tuatara, are able to shed their tails in case of emergency. This procedure is an example of autotomy, or self-mutilation. Its value is obvious to anyone who has tried to grab a lizard and has been left with only a piece of violently wriggling tail in his hand while the animal scuttles to safety. Active contraction of the tail muscles plays a large part in bringing about the fracture, and in some lizards the tail may seem to fly off almost before the creature has actually been grasped.

The ability to shed the tail in this way depends on the presence of a series of weak spots, or fracture planes, in the tail substance. These planes pass through the bodies of the individual vertebræ and not between two vertebræ, as one might expect, and they can be seen in prepared skeletons as partial splits in the bone. As the break occurs, the surrounding muscles separate neatly at the fibrous partition between two of the segmented muscle blocks with very little loss of blood.

Most lizards which can break off their tails are able to grow new ones, but the regenerated structure is not a perfect copy of the old. Thus the separate bony vertebræ are replaced only by a rod of cartilage and the spinal cord is not properly replaced. Moreover the scales covering the new tail may be abnormal in appearance, and regeneration of double or even triple tails is occasionally seen. In certain species of lizards, the limbs also have some power of regeneration, an abnormal cone-like outgrowth sometimes forming at the site of amputation.

Male lizards and snakes possess twin genitalia called hemipenes (Fig. 22, p. 108), although only one or other of these organs is used at a time. The hemipenes are attached to the walls of the cloacal chamber and, when not in action, are withdrawn into the base of the tail. Their presence can be detected by a slight swelling in this region, which may help one to recognise the male. Each organ is shaped rather like a bag with thick walls which, in the act of coitus, is turned inside out and protruded from the cloaca. This 'tumescence', as it is called, is caused by the combined action of muscles and blood vessels which fill up and cause the walls to swell; the sperm is then carried along a groove in the organ to the oviduct of the female. In many snakes each hemipenis is forked, and furnished with spines which anchor it in the female's cloaca. Variations in the appearance of the hemipenes are a useful guide in classification.

In many lizards a number of small raised spots known as femoral pores can be seen on the under surface of the thighs (Fig. 15). These are formed from the heaped-up secretions of little gland-like organs which lie beneath them. They give the skin a rough surface and probably help to prevent the cloacal regions of the male and female lizard from slipping apart during the sexual act. They may be present in both sexes, as in the lacertids, or only in the males, and in some lizards such as many geckos, there are similar structures called pre-anal pores on the scales in front of the cloacal opening. These pores, also, may be useful in identification.

The social and sexual life of lizards is exceptionally

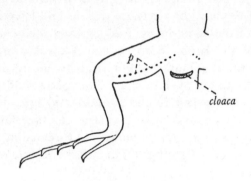

FIG. 15

Under-surface of thigh of lizard, showing position of femoral pores (*p*).

interesting and complex. The two sexes often differ strikingly in behaviour, colour and form as do many species of birds. The males are generally larger than the females, with broader and more massive heads; they are also more aggressive and conspicuous. The bright colours of the males of many species often become even more pronounced in the breeding season, probably owing to the activity of the sex glands. These differences are particularly noticeable in the agamid and iguanid groups, where the males are also often distinguished by the presence of crests, throat pouches and other appendages. These lizards are large-eyed, diurnal creatures, and as experiments with painted models have shown, they recognise each other's sex almost entirely by sight.

During the breeding season the male lizards occupy territories such as a stretch of wall or a tree-stump which they share with a number of females and young. Other males which try to encroach on the territory or harem are attacked and usually driven off by the tenant. When confronting their fellows these lizards perform various gestures, each appropriate to the particular occasion, as when one male challenges another, or greets a female. Vigorous bobbing of the head or alternate raising and lowering of the front part of the body on the fore-legs are often conspicuous elements of the ritual. Some types of display are accompanied by rapid colour changes, and by the raising of the crest and dilatation of the throat. This pattern of behaviour is particularly marked in the agamid and iguanid lizards, and is usually less obvious in lizards of other families. In encounters between rival males a threatening display, rather than actual fighting, often suffices to put one of the two to flight.

The act of mating in lizards is often preceded by a brief courtship, the male nudging and biting the female, or touching her with his tongue. Finally, he seizes her with his jaws by the neck or flank and twists the hinder part of his body beneath hers so that the cloacæ of the two animals are brought into contact (Fig. 16), and one of his hemipenes can be inserted.

So much, then, for generalities; we must now consider some of the more typical and interesting members of the lizard group. If we turn to the classification in Appendix B (p. 142) we shall see that the lizards form the suborder Lacertilia (or Sauria) of the order Squamata, and can be divided into some eighteen families. Their closest relations are the tuatara (which has a whole order to itself but which, for the sake of simplicity, will be dealt with at the end of this chapter) and the snakes, to be dealt with in Chapter 4.

For people who have spent time in hot countries the most familiar of all lizards are certainly the geckos (family Gekkonidæ). This is because some species have adapted themselves very well to human activities, and have taken to living in houses, old walls and other buildings. We have even heard

FIG. 16

Mating posture of teiid lizards (*Ameiva chrysolaema*). Adapted from G. K. Noble and H. T. Bradley, 1933, *Annals of the New York Academy of Sciences*, vol. 35, p. 32, by John Norris Wood.

of a gecko in Ceylon that would descend from its lair in the evening when people were having drinks, climb up a glass and take a sip of the contents. The sympathetic character of this family of lizards could hardly be better exemplified.

The appearance of the commoner types of gecko is quite unmistakable. They are mostly small creatures and indeed include the smallest lizards known—certain species of *Sphærodactylus* from the West Indies which are under two inches long. At the other end of the scale is the tokay (*Gekko gecko*; plate 4a) from south-east Asia, a stoutly built lizard about a foot in length. The head of most geckos is rather large, bluntly oval in outline and, like the body, flattened somewhat from above downwards. The scales on the back are very small, and the skin is soft and thin so that some species have an almost translucent appearance when seen in strong light. The colours are usually dull, though in certain forms the back and tail are strikingly banded. Among the few really brilliant members of the group are the diurnal geckos (*Phelsuma*) from east Africa and some islands in the Indian Ocean, which are vivid green on the back with red spots and streaks. These lizards are able to change colour, and become almost black when placed in the dark.

Most geckos are active at night or in the evening, and their eyes show many interesting features. In the great majority they are covered by a spectacle instead of movable eyelids. In many species the pupils are slit-shaped, and the edges of the slit are notched so that when they are brought together a series of tiny openings remain (Fig. 14c, p. 65). This arrangement probably enables a gecko to see sharply even when its pupils are fully contracted and the minimum of light is entering the eye. It is probably of special value in species such as *Tarentola mauritanica*, a common gecko on both sides of the Mediterranean, which are active in the evening but also sometimes bask in the sun or come into the light to catch insects.

Geckos are noisy creatures and their name is derived from the chirping and clicking sounds which they make when they emerge in the evening from their crannies. Their inner ears are very highly developed, and sounds seem to play a greater part in their lives than in those of other lizards. Possibly the voice is used as a substitute for the posture and display carried out by many lizards during courtship and when defending territory. Little is known, however, about the social life of geckos, except that many species are gregarious.

Many geckos are excellently adapted for climbing on rocks and walls and their skill in running up completely smooth surfaces is well known. Some species can even scale a sheet of glass or cling upside down to a ceiling. Their powers of climbing depend on a remarkable mechanism. In many species, such as the eastern house geckos (*Hemidactylus*), each toe ends in a sharp backward curving claw, behind which is an expanded region known as the pad. On the underside of the pad are a number of large scales, or lamellæ, furnished with minute hair-like projections which fit into irregularities in the surface (Fig. 17a). Combined with the action of the claws, these enable the gecko to adhere to it. Certain African tree geckos (*Lygodactylus*) have a similar friction pad beneath the tip of the tail. The gecko's ability to hold on by such means has recently led a leading book reviewer of a London paper to say of a certain thriller that it "gripped like a gecko" No author of this type of book could ask for higher praise.

A further adaption of the gecko foot is found in the 'flying' geckos (*Ptychozoon*) from south-east Asia, which have their toes joined by broad webs. In combination with prominent fringes along the flanks and tail these help the animal to parachute gently from a tree to the ground. There are also a number of ground geckos which lack friction pads. In desert-living species the toes may have scaly fringes, or webs which act like snowshoes as the lizard moves across the sand (Fig. 17b). The feet of geckos are obviously very adaptable structures and the variations which they show (in the arrangement of the lamellæ, for example) are useful in classification. This is why the names of so many genera have the termination –*dactylus*, meaning a toe or finger.

Nearly all geckos are oviparous and their eggs, unlike those of other lizards, generally become hard and brittle soon after being laid. They are generally laid in pairs and left in crevices or under bark. Like the adults, the eggs may be carried overseas in floating vegetation or on ships, and it is probable that the very wide distribution of the group is partly due to such methods of dispersal.

Two small families of lizards that are probably related to the geckos are the Xantusiidæ of America and the Pygopodidæ of Australasia. The former are small, rather gecko-like but viviparous lizards, while the latter are snake-like in

form with rudimentary limbs; in some species the hind pair
are visible as small scaly flaps. Little is known of the habits of
pygopods, but some are specialised for burrowing.

The iguanid and agamid families (Iguanidæ and Aga-
midæ) contain a varied assortment of lizards, some very big,
others small and nimble, but they include no snake-like types.

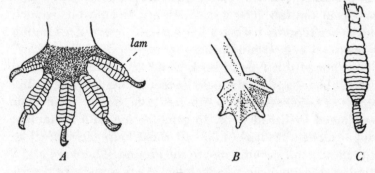

FIG. 17

A, Foot of gecko *Hemidactylus flaviviridis* from below, showing lamellae
(*lam*) on friction pads (after B. C. Mahendra, 1941, *Proceedings of the
Indian Academy of Sciences*, vol. 13, p. 294).
B, 'Snow-shoe' foot (left front) of desert-living *Palmatagecko rangei
from above.* (After J. Procter, 1929, *Proceedings of the Zoological Society
of London*, p. 918.)
C, Right hind third toe of *Anolis* sp. from below, showing friction pad.

In habits they may be terrestrial, tree-living or amphibious,
and the great majority lay eggs. Many of them have crests,
bright and often changeable colours, and other adornments
which may only be present in the males. As we have seen
(p. 70) their social life is often elaborate. Iguanids are found
mainly in America, and agamids in Africa, Asia and Australasia, but the two groups are closely related and, except in
tooth structure (p. 61), resemble each other in many ways.

The big iguanas live mainly in America and the West
Indies. The common species (*Iguana iguana*; Plate 4b), often
seen in zoos, is an impressive bright green reptile with blackish

markings which grows over five feet in length. The crest of horny spines along its back and its large spiny dewlap gives it a distinctly dragonish aspect which is sometimes exploited by trick photography in science fiction films. It frequents trees over water in which it can dive when disturbed, and eats both plant and animal food. It is itself eaten by some American Indians, who hunt it with dogs and esteem its flesh as a great delicacy.

The sea iguana (*Amblyrhynchus cristatus*; Plate 3b) of the Galapagos Islands deserves a special place in the history of herpetology for, like the giant tortoises, it attracted the attention of Charles Darwin when he visited these remote and desolate islands. This four-foot reptile, clothed in scales as black and rugged as the lava rocks among which it lives, is the only existing type of marine lizard. It swims beautifully by means of its long, vertically flattened tail, but seldom goes far from land. Even when frightened it prefers to wedge itself into a rocky crevice than take refuge in the water. Darwin suggested that the cause of this behaviour might be, that apart from man, it has no enemies on land, whereas in the sea it must sometimes be attacked by sharks. It is itself quite harmless, and feeds entirely on seaweed, exposed at low tide in the surf. Like most of its relatives the sea iguana has quite an elaborate social life. Rival males indulge in jousts of an almost ceremonial character for territory or females. These are conducted in a most gentlemanly fashion, not by biting, but by butting and pushing. Although neither of the contestants gets seriously hurt the weaker eventually beats a retreat.

The Galapagos are also the home of another kind of big iguana, *Conolophus subcristatus*, which lives entirely on land and feeds on cactus. It is sad to read in Dr Eibl-Eibesfeldt's fascinating book on the Galapagos (see Bibliography) that the sea and land iguanas, like the giant tortoises, are still menaced by wanton human destructiveness. Let us wish every success for the recent project to establish a permanent nature reserve and research station on these wonderful islands, so that the future of their grand reptiles can be assured.

In the forests of Central America live a group of large

FIG. 18

Basilisk (*Basiliscus basiliscus*) running at speed on its hind legs. The tail acts as a counterbalance to the body. (From a cine-photo in an article by R. C. Snyder, 1949, *Copeia*, p. 136). Drawing by W. Graham.

tree-lizards known as basilisks (*Basiliscus*; Fig. 18), which are closely related to the iguanas. The males have a large helmet-like crest on the head and also crests on the back and tail, but the smaller females lack these flamboyant adornments. When moving fast the basilisk runs on its hind legs, its thick heavy tail acting as a counterpoise. Its ability to run in this way for several yards across a stream supported entirely by the surface tension is apparently authenticated.

Among the best known of the many smaller iguanids are the tree-lizards of the genus *Anolis* (Plate 6a). There are over 160 species of these small brightly coloured creatures which possess expanded climbing pads on their toes (Fig. 17c) similar in function, as well as in structure, to those of geckos. One species is even able to parachute with their aid in a manner reminiscent of the flying geckos and flying dragons of south-east Asia. Male anoles have a large and conspicuous fan-like structure beneath the throat which can be rapidly dilated by a complex mechanism of skeleton and muscle. These lizards are almost as good at colour change as the chamæleons (p. 79), and, in fact, the name chamæleon is often erroneously applied to *Anolis carolinensis*, the common North American species. In body colour this lizard ranges from dark brown to vivid emerald green. When the throat of the male is dilated in courtship or combat it becomes a brilliant pinkish red. The effect is not due to pigment changes, such as occur on the body, but to the sudden exposure, by stretching, of red areas of skin between the scales of the dewlap.

The little horned 'toads' (*Phrynosoma*) of the North American deserts are quite different in appearance from the other iguanids, having squat toad-like bodies and short tails. They are well armed with spines on the head and body, and have the peculiar ability to squirt thin jets of blood from their eyes. This may irritate the eyes, and so put an aggressor off his stroke. They feed on insects, mainly ants, which they lick up voraciously with their flat tongues.

The likeness between the iguanids and some of the agamids, now to be described, is often quite remarkable. For instance, the iguanid horned toads mentioned in the previous paragraph are very like the agamid 'thorny devils' (*Moloch*) of Australia (Plate 3a). Other large agamids show an equally close resemblance to their iguanid cousins: for example, the three-foot water dragon (*Physignathus lesueuri*) from Australia and the equally large sailed dragon (*Lophura*) from the East Indies are counterparts of the big iguanas. *Lophura* has crests on the back and tail somewhat like those of the basilisk.

An even more striking agamid is the frilled lizard (*Chlamydosaurus*; Plate 5a), which has a dramatic frill-like structure round the neck which can be suddenly erected when the creature is threatened. A related form known as the bearded lizard (*Amphibolurus barbatus*) has a ruff on the under surface of the throat. The frilled lizards, like the basilisks, are exceptionally good at moving about on their hind legs.

Among the many other members of the agamid family are the heavily built spiny-tailed lizards (*Uromastix*) of north Africa and north-western India. These are gentle herbivorous creatures which make burrows in the desert sand. The family also contains many smaller and more active lizards of the genus *Agama* which are found over most of the warmer parts of the Old World. The common oriental tree-lizards of the genus *Calotes* are also agamids, and one species, known as *Calotes versicolor*, is particularly spectacular. The head and throat of the males of this lizard can turn bright scarlet, a condition which has caused it to be given the graphic, if rather repellant, name of 'bloodsucker'.

Perhaps the most remarkable of all the agamids are the flying dragons (*Draco*; Fig. 19) of south-eastern Asia. These can take long gliding leaps through the air by means of wing-like extensions of the skin along the flanks. Unlike the fringes of the 'flying' geckos, these 'wings' are supported by the ribs and can be spread or folded at will, though they cannot, of course, be flapped like the wings of a bird. In some species they are brightly coloured and used in courtship as well as in flight. Beneath the throat is a large wattle-like appendage which is said to be erected in display, but folded flat during flight. There is a smaller flap-like appendage on each side. These little creatures, generally under a foot in length, have been likened to butterflies as they dart among the branches, with their bright wings opening and closing in the sunlight.

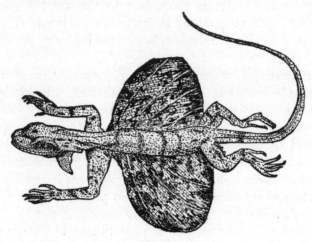

FIG. 19

Flying dragon (*Draco* sp.) with wings extended.

The chamæleons (family Chameleontidæ) are very special-ised tree-lizards which are probably descended from agamid ancestors. The majority of chamæleon species are found in Africa and Madagascar, but there is one in India and another in North Africa, Spain and certain Mediterranean islands. In size they range from dwarfs only a few inches long, some of which conceal themselves by looking like leaves, to giants of about two feet. In many species the top of the head is raised into a high bony casque, and in some there are horns on the snout and forehead. These are particularly well developed in the males, and may be used in fighting. Chamæleons cling to the branches by means of their prehensile tails and their curious feet which are excellently modified for efficient grasping. The fingers and toes of each limb are webbed and arranged in two opposable groups, so that they can obtain an exceptionally firm grasp. Many species of chamæleons lay eggs which are buried in the soil. A considerable number, however, for example some of those which live in the central African highlands, are viviparous. In some chamæleons, at least, the gestation period seems to be unusually long, perhaps a year.

The means by which chamæleons capture their prey is a remarkable example of the co-ordinated adaptation of many different organs. The huge and extremely efficient eyes, surrounded by curious cone-shaped eyelids, can be swivelled independently in any direction, giving the maximum field of vision. Once an insect has been sighted the two eyes converge, bringing it under binocular observation. The chamæleon then slowly stalks its prey until it is within range of the tongue, which in some species is as long as the body and tail. The tongue is next pulled forward to the front of the mouth and poised there for a moment before being shot out to catch the insect on its sticky expanded tip (Plate 5b). The projection of the tongue is brought about by a specialised muscular mechanism.

The chamæleon's ability to change colour has become proverbial. As in other animals with the same talent, the process is due to changes in the position of small pigment granules within certain cells of the skin. Colour change in chamæleons seems to be controlled mainly by the nervous system, whereas in the *Anolis* lizards the secretions of the pituitary gland are the principal agent. Usually chamæleons assume colours which blend with their surroundings, but when fighting or threatened they put on brilliant displays of colour change. At such times they often flatten their bodies from side to side or inflate themselves with air, increasing their apparent size; they also hiss with gaping mouths. Background, lighting, temperature and 'emotional state' are all important in influencing colour change.

These attractive reptiles have a reputation for doing badly in captivity, but some species at least will flourish if given a plentiful supply of food. Dwarf chamæleons such as *Microsaura pumila*, a viviparous form from south Africa, are particularly recommended as pets; they require less food than the larger species and sometimes breed in the vivarium.

English people, if they think about lizards at all, generally have a member of the family Lacertidæ in mind. The lacertids are the only limbed lizards which inhabit this country, and are also those most commonly seen on a visit to France or Italy. They are, in fact, widespread throughout the Old World, but do not occur in America. All the lacertids are active, four-legged diurnal creatures which can run quickly, climb well, dig a little and even swim a little. In general, however, they are not highly specialised for any one of these activities.

The common lizard (*Lacerta vivipara*) is found on heaths and banks throughout the British Isles and much of northern Europe, and is the only reptile found in Ireland. It is usually brownish in colour with a lighter belly and reaches a maximum length of about seven inches. It feeds on insects and other small creatures, especially spiders.

Unlike most other members of the lacertid family, the common lizard bears its young alive, although quite often they are born within their membranes and do not escape from them for some hours (see p. 34). One instance has been reported, however, of this reptile laying eggs in the manner of typical oviparous lizards. A large number of eggs apparently belonging to this species were found some years ago at one place in the Pyrenees. They had parchment-like shells and contained embryos at varying stages of development, suggesting that they had been laid by several

81

females. Some of the eggs hatched, so that correct identification of the young should have been possible. This very
interesting observation suggests that in certain parts of its
range the common lizard may have retained the primitive
egg-laying habit instead of becoming viviparous. Unfortunately this is still unconfirmed by later accounts of similar
instances, and it would be unwise to generalise on the basis
of this single report.

The sand lizard (*Lacerta agilis*) is a slightly larger and
much more handsome reptile than the common lizard, and
is likewise found in many parts of Europe. In England it
has only a local distribution, mainly on sandy heaths in
Hampshire, Dorset and adjoining counties, and in one part
of Lancashire. It lays eggs in a shallow hole in the ground,
or under a stone. The males are very pugnacious during
the breeding season and develop a vivid green colouring
along the flanks which sometimes causes them to be mistaken
for the green lizard.

The wall lizard (*Lacerta muralis*) is another small and very
agile species common in Europe, especially round the
Mediterranean, where many different races exist. It is not
a native of the British Isles, except for Jersey, but two small
colonies artificially introduced into the south of England
are known to have maintained themselves for at least twenty
years.

The green lizard (*Lacerta viridis*), one of the most beautiful
of all reptiles, is often sold in pet shops, and may grow
nearly eighteen inches long. It is found in many localities
on the mainland of Europe but does not occur naturally in
the British Isles. It can, however, be seen on Jersey and
Guernsey, where it often inhabits cliffs overlooking the sea.
In captivity it does well, at least for a time, but needs a
variety of insect food, and also likes an occasional slice of
tomato or orange. Several attempts have been made to
introduce the green lizard to Britain, but none of the arti-

ficial colonies have so far survived for more than a few years.

The eyed lizard (*Lacerta lepida*) from southern Europe and north Africa is another handsome species. It is bright green with blue spots, along the neck and flanks which are ringed with black. This powerful lizard grows to a length of at least two feet and is able to tackle mice and smaller lizards as well as insects. Several other kinds of lacertid such as *Takydromus* and *Acanthodactylus* (the latter a desert form with scale-fringed toes somewhat like those of the sand geckos) are found in southern Europe, Africa and Asia.

The family Teiidæ is restricted to America, and corresponds in some ways with the Lacertidæ of the Old World, though its members show a greater range of size, shape and habits. There are a few limbless forms and many small, active four-legged ones, such as the ameivas, and the race-runners (*Cnemidophorus*). The family also includes the tegus (*Tupinambis*) of South America, powerful carnivorous lizards over a yard long which resemble the monitors in habits, and likewise possess long, deeply forked tongues. The caiman lizard (*Dracæna guianensis*) of British Guiana and the Amazon is an even larger creature with bony plates down its back like a crocodile. It is amphibious and feeds on shellfish, which it crushes with its very broad, blunt teeth.

Southern Africa is the home of the girdle-tailed lizards or zonures, long known as the Zonuridæ, but now usually called by the family name Cordylidæ (Plate 6b). The largest representative of the group is about fifteen inches long. These lizards have developed a remarkable armour of spines which in some species is confined to the tail, and in others is present also on the head and body. This armour is a useful means of defence, for not only does it make the lizards hard to swallow, but it also enables them to wedge themselves very securely into crevices among the crags on which they live. One very spiny species, *Cordylus cataphractus*, assumes a rather charming armadillo-like defence posture when caught in the open, curling up on its back with its tail in its mouth and its limbs held in front of its belly. This is illustrated by Walter Rose in his book on *The Reptiles and Amphibians of Southern Africa*.

Zonures are fond of basking in the heat of the sun on rocky outcrops on the veldt. They feed mainly on insects, and are viviparous, producing only one to four young at a time. The family also includes some atypical, nearly limbless types belonging to the genus *Chamæsaura*.

The African plated lizards (*Gerrhosaurus*) belong to the same family as the zonures, but their scales, instead of being spiny, are like small flat plates touching at their edges to give a mosaic effect. The bony plates, or osteoderms (see p. 21), beneath these scales are well developed, enclosing the whole body in a firm but movable suit of armour. To compensate for the rigidity of their coats these lizards have a deep lateral fold or groove along each flank which presumably allows for distension after a meal, or when the mother lizard is carrying her eggs. Similar, though less conspicuous, folds can be seen in many other lizards. As in the cordylids and skinks there are some forms such as *Tetradactylus* in which the limbs are reduced.

The skink family (Scincidæ) is one of the biggest groups of lizards. Its members are found all over the world and are often very common, but as most of them are small and inconspicuous they attract little popular notice. Many live on the ground among stones, sand or fallen leaves, and quite a large number are burrowers.

A 'typical' skink, if one can use the word of such a widely differentiated family, is a streamlined lizard with a small head, a hardly perceptible neck, a long body and short limbs. The whole animal is covered with smooth, shiny scales which give it a slippery appearance. The colour is often brownish with longitudinal stripes, or spots, although some species are more strikingly marked.

Many skinks of this type belong to the genera *Eumeces*, *Mabuya* and *Scincus*. The last genus contains desert forms which have fringed toes and eardrums covered by flaps of skin as an adaptation to this environment. They burrow so quickly in the sand that they almost seem to swim into it and, with certain other species, are spoken of in north Africa as *poissons du sable*. The mabuyas, a very widely distributed group, live mostly under stones and vegetation. Some species have a window in the lower eyelid, and in a related genus, *Ablepharus*, there is a complete spectacle. Most of the biggest members of the skink family, such as the giant skink (*Egernia major*), the blue-tongued lizard (*Tiliqua scincoides*), and the shingle-back (*Tiliqua rugosa*), which has rough scales and a short, stumpy tail, are found in Australia. These are bulky lizards with an average length of one to two feet, which live on both plant and insect food. *Egernia stokesi* (Plate 7a) is a smaller Australian species.

The skinks provide some of the most striking examples of limb degeneration among lizards, and in certain genera all degrees of degeneration can be seen. Let us consider, for example, the *Chalcides* group, which live mainly in southern Europe and north Africa. One member of this genus, *Chalcides ocellatus*, is a 'typical' skink with four well developed if somewhat short legs, each provided with five digits. In several of its relations, however, the number of digits have been reduced to four. In *Chalcides tridactylus* the process of limb degeneration is carried further still, for it has minute legs with only three toes on each. Finally, in at least one species the limbs consist only of tiny undivided stumps. Similar series are found in other genera, and sometimes culminate in forms with no external limbs at all. Most of these skinks are burrowers, or live among grass roots or

85

under stones and logs, and have reduced eyes and ears as well as limbs.

The majority of skinks bear their young alive, and some, such as *Chalcides tridactylus*, have perhaps the most advanced types of placenta (p. 35) found in reptiles. Walter Rose refers to the birth of the young in one of the south African mabuyas, describing how the mother assists the babies to escape from their embryonic coverings by tearing these open with her mouth. Rather similar habits have been noticed in the night lizards (*Xantusia*) which belong to a different family (p. 73).

We have seen that reptiles do not often give any degree of parental care to their young (p. 33), but, like the example just quoted, certain American skinks of the genus *Eumeces* are also notable exceptions to the rule. Unlike most of their relations these particular skinks lay eggs, which are hidden immediately under bark or loose earth. The female then remains near them during the whole of the incubation period, turning them at regular intervals with her nose and, in some species, defending them against mice and other small creatures. In experiments conducted with these lizards it was found that the female would normally accept and brood the eggs of lizards of the same genus, but not those of unrelated species. Nor, very properly, would she have anything to do with artificial eggs, or her own if they had been covered with shellac. She could locate and recognise her own eggs even when she was blindfolded, the tongue and Jacobson's organs probably being the main sense organs involved. Perhaps an even more remarkable example of maternal care is provided by the female of the related species, *Eumeces obsoletus*. In this case the mother retains an interest in her babies for as long as ten days after hatching, and periodically grooms the tiny skinklets by licking their cloacal regions.

Scientists interested in burrowing animals are always particularly intrigued by the worm-lizards (family Amphisbænidæ) of southern Europe, Africa and America. These are sometimes classified with the skinks, but they differ in so many ways from other lizards that they should perhaps be placed in a major group, such as a suborder, of their own. Travesties of these creatures figure in the medieval bestiaries and the idea that they possessed a head at either end was a particularly common superstition of the time. It was doubtless inspired by the fact that in many species the tail is very short and stumpy, and looks rather like the almost eyeless head.

Most amphisbænids are under two feet long and look like big earthworms. Externally there are no legs, except in the Mexican genus *Bipes*, which has an improbable-looking pair of short front limbs sticking out behind the head. The scales are arranged in rings around the body, and by moving these in a co-ordinated fashion amphisbænids are able to hitch themselves along without going into serpentine undulations. They can also move backwards in this way as well as forwards, and owe their scientific name (which means 'going both ways') to this notable accomplishment.

The amphisbænid head is used for ramming the soil in burrowing, and the skull shows several important adaptations to this function. It is extremely solid and compact and the edges of the skull-roof bones interlock to give extra strength. The snout may be either blunt and rounded, or flattened like a shovel or, as in the genus *Anops*, compressed from side to side to form a wedge. The ear-drums are absent and the eyes rudimentary, although in most species they are probably at least sensitive to light.

Amphisbænids live almost entirely underground and little is known of their habits. They feed mainly on worms and insects, and sometimes frequent the nests of ants and termites. Some lay eggs, but others are probably viviparous.

The next family we must discuss is scientifically known as the Anguidæ, a word which implies snake-lizards. The name is misleading, however, as the group includes the American alligator lizards (*Gerrhonotus*), which have well-developed limbs, as well as such limbless and superficially snake-like lizards as the slow-worm. The members of the family Xenosauridæ, which are closely related to the anguids, and include only a few poorly known Mexican lizards and one from China, also possess well-developed legs.

Alligator lizards are usually under eighteen inches long, but their broad back scales and rather elongated bodies give them a rather far-fetched resemblance to alligators. Some species have a specially interesting means of defence; the lizard encircles a branch with its tail in its mouth to prevent an enemy from dragging it away. Certain other members of the family are in some ways intermediate between the alligator lizards and the limbless slow-worm; their legs are short, or rudimentary, and they progress by wriggling.

The slow-worm (*Anguis fragilis*; Plate 7b) is the third species of lizard found in Great Britain; it also has a wide range on the continent of Europe. Like the common lizard, it is often found on banks and heaths, sometimes in the open and sometimes beneath stones and logs. It can burrow in soft soil and is occasionally unearthed in compost heaps. It is less fond of heat than either the common or sand lizards, though it may sometimes be found basking in the early morning sun. Its body, usually between ten and sixteen inches long, is covered with smooth, brownish, shiny scales which make it look like a bar of polished, flexible metal. Some specimens have their normal metallic colour varied with flecks of blue on the back. The eyes are small, though perfectly functional, and the ear-opening absent or so minute as to be hardly visible. The tail is shed readily, but has only limited powers of regeneration, so that little more than a conical stump is usually formed.

The main food of the slow-worm consists of earthworms

and slugs, but its sharp, curved teeth are curiously formidable for such a diet. They are used, however, in fighting, which takes place between the males at the start of the breeding season. But even when picked up, the animals seldom if ever bite the human hand. The young are usually born in August or September, the average litter being from six to twelve. The little wormlets are exceptionally attractive creatures about three inches long. Their backs are golden brown or silvery with a thin black stripe down the middle, while the belly and flanks are jet black. The slow-worm's relative, the glass 'snake' (*Ophisaurus*) of America and southern Europe, is a much larger creature which sometimes attains a length of three feet or more. Unlike the slow-worm, the members of this genus lay eggs, and the American *Ophisaurus ventralis* has been seen to brood them in her coils.

A family closely related to the anguids is the Anniellidæ, which contains only two species, one being the little Californian lizard *Anniella pulchra*, a limbless creature looking rather like a slow-worm. It is, however, much more highly adapted for burrowing life and is seldom seen above ground.

Perhaps the most imposing of all living lizards are the monitors of the family Varanidæ. They are found in Africa, throughout most of the East, and in Australia, but not on the American continent. They are often spoken of as 'iguanas', which is corrupted in Australia to 'goannas'. But they have little in common with the real iguanas of America except that some of them reach a large size—the largest, in fact, attained by any modern lizards. Their skins are much in demand for making into shoes and handbags, and their flesh forms part of the diet of some native peoples.

In appearance nearly all the different kinds of monitor are much alike, and they are placed in the single genus *Varanus*. They are long, sinuous beasts without spiny crests or dewlaps, and usually have subdued colours, at least in the adult. Their tails are long and powerful, and in the more water-loving types are somewhat flattened in the vertical plane so that they can be used as paddles in swimming. The tails are also used in defence to give slashing blows and, as the vertebræ lack fracture planes (p. 67), they cannot easily be broken off. The feet are armed with strong claws and, unlike most lizards, the animals may use them to hold down and tear their prey.

The tongues of monitors are long, deeply forked and retractible like the tongues of snakes. They are constantly being flicked in and out so that the animal can explore its surroundings by means of the organs of Jacobson (p. 63). The senses of sight and hearing are also well developed, and by human standards monitors seem more alert and intelligent than most lizards. They have a characteristic habit of rearing up the front of their bodies on their fore-legs, then turning their heads on their long necks and looking deliberately about them.

In spite of their general similarity, the different species of monitor (about thirty in all) vary somewhat in habits and habitat. Some, such as the white-throated monitor (*Varanus albigularis*) of southern Africa, an unusually thickset species, live in dry rocky country, while others, such as the water monitor (*Varanus salvator*) of India and the East Indies, prefer marshy and wooded areas. Most species climb and swim well, and some can run extremely fast over open ground. The Komodo dragon (*Varanus komodœnsis*) is the giant of the group and, with a length of ten feet, is the biggest living lizard. The water monitor, the Nile monitor (*Varanus niloticus*; Plate 8a) and the perentie (*Varanus giganteus*) of northern and central Australia are likewise very large lizards, growing to between five to eight feet long. There are also many three to five foot species such as *Varanus monitor*, which is common in India and Burma, and a few comparative dwarfs.

The Komodo dragon, by its enormous size alone, is the most spectacular of all living lizards. Its range is limited to

Komodo and a few neighbouring islands in the East Indies, where it was first discovered in 1910. In that year a Dutch army officer was intrigued by rumours that a giant reptile resembling the typical dragon of the story books lurked in the jungles of the region. Accordingly he set out in search of the creature and eventually managed to shoot two specimens. Later a number of these impressive dragons began to reach European zoos where, in spite of their formidable appearance, they proved to be most gentle and attractive creatures. In fact both the present authors remember a famous pair which reached the London Zoo in 1927 and were so docile that they could be patted like dogs.

In spite of their tolerant attitude to humans when captive, however, the Komodo dragon in the wild is not a creature to treat with disrespect. It is quite capable of killing small pigs and deer, and is even reputed to be a man-killer on occasion, although this must be taken with a pinch of salt. Its predatory habits are typical of monitors, which are the only modern lizards which have become really effective as beasts of prey. Though all members of the group feed a good deal on insects and other invertebrates, they also eat amphibians, other reptiles, birds, small mammals and carrion. They are fond of birds' eggs and sometimes raid chicken runs to obtain them, while some species take a heavy toll of the eggs of crocodiles and turtles. In most monitors the teeth are sharp and recurved, and since the animals hang on grimly to their victims they can inflict serious bites. In a few forms such as the Nile monitor, however, the teeth become increasingly blunt and peglike with age, not merely as the result of wear, but owing to a progressive change in the character of succeeding tooth generations. Such teeth are very suitable for crushing crabs and snails which form a substantial part of the diet of this species.

Little is known of the social life of monitors, though in some species the males are known to fight in a spectacular fashion, rearing up on their hind legs and grappling with each other with their front claws. All of them lay eggs, and some species have the habit of laying them in termite nests, which by reason of their constant temperature and humidity make excellent natural incubators.

The monitors are an ancient family whose history goes back more than seventy million years when certain of their relatives, a group of huge marine lizards known as mosasaurs, were terrorising the seas. Today the closest living allies of the monitors are a rare lizard from Borneo known as *Lanthanotus* (the 'earless monitor'), and the heloderms, the only poisonous lizards now alive.

There are two species of heloderm with the ominous scientific names of *Heloderma suspectum* and *Heloderma horridum* (Plate 8b). *Heloderma suspectum*, the Gila monster, occurs in Arizona and adjacent regions and was featured in Walt Disney's famous film *The Living Desert*. It is a heavily built lizard, sometimes reaching a length of nearly two feet, with a massive head, short tail and raised, bead-like scales. Its black and orange or pink markings are sometimes regarded as an example of warning coloration, but seem to be mainly designed for concealment. In spite of its vivid colours the animal is quite hard to see among the sand and stone of its natural haunts, especially at night.

Although the Gila monster inhabits regions which may be called deserts, it is not adapted for really high temperatures, and is commonest among rocky foothills where there is some vegetation and a fairly heavy seasonal rainfall. It is most active after dark during the hottest and wettest months, and retires to its burrow during the heat of the day. During the colder months, which are usually dry, it hibernates, conserving its water supply, and can survive long periods of drought and starvation. It lays large eggs, each about two and a half inches long, in a hole in the sand. In its movements it is slow and deliberate, and feeds mainly on

9a. Tuatara (*Sphenodon punctatus*).

9b. Whip snake (*Dryophis prasinus*) of India and South-east Asia.

10a. Boomslang (*Dispholidus typus*) inflating throat.

10b. Mulga snake (*Pseudechis australis*), a poisonous snake from Australia.

1a. Worm-or blind-snake (*Typhlops unguirostris*). This species is from Australia.

1b. Boa constrictor (*Constrictor constrictor*).

12a. Adder (*Vipera berus*).

12b. Gaboon viper (*Bitis gabonica*).

birds' eggs with the occasional fledgling or baby rodent. It is not in the least aggressive but hangs on tenaciously when finally provoked to bite. Its venom, which seems to be used primarily for defensive purposes, will kill small animals quite quickly in the laboratory, but the apparatus for injecting it is not very efficient. Its poison glands are in the lower jaw instead of the upper as in snakes, and discharge their venom along grooves in the mandibular teeth; strangely enough the teeth of the upper jaw, where there are no poison glands, are grooved also. There is much disagreement about the effects of its bite on human beings. An exhaustive survey of the problem by two north American herpetologists, Bogert and del Campo (p. 145), reaches the conclusion that only about eight human beings may actually have been killed by it, and some of these seem to have been drunk or otherwise in bad shape at the time. Pain and swelling are often the only effects of a bite, but sometimes the heart and respiratory system are affected, which could have dangerous consequences.

The other species of heloderm, *Heloderma horridum*, popularly known as the escorpión, is found in Mexico. It may grow nearly a yard long, and generally has white or yellowish, instead of pink or orange markings. Its habits are probably similar to those of the Gila monster, but since it lives in less accessible regions fewer herpetologists have been moved to record them.

With these brief notes about the heloderms we come to the end of our account of the true lizards. We have decided, however, for the sake of simplicity, to include in this chapter our description of that exceptionally interesting reptile from New Zealand known as the tuatara (*Sphenodon punctatus*; Plate 9a). This is not strictly a lizard at all, and in fact differs sufficiently in its anatomy from the other creatures we have been describing to be assigned not only to a different family, but even to a different order, the Rhynchocephalia, or 'beak-heads'. Nevertheless it is so lizard-like in appearance that it may legitimately be considered here. Up-to-date knowledge of the creature's habits owes much to the work of W. H. Dawbin of the University of Sydney, who has spent many years studying it in the wild.

The word tuatara means spine-bearing in the Maori language, and a glance at Plate 9a will show why the animal got its name. The scientific name *Sphenodon* means 'wedge-tooth', and is derived from the shape of the very large chisel-like teeth at the front of the upper and lower jaws. In general appearance the tuatara looks like a clumsy, big-headed lizard, olive-brownish in colour with a spiny crest on the back of the head and down its back. Its main difference from the true lizards is connected with certain technicalities in the structure of the skull, and also in the fact that the male has no hemipenes, but transmits its sperm to the female by direct cloacal contact. The males, incidentally, can grow to about two feet in length, but the females are considerably smaller. As in many lizards, the tail can be shed and a new one, of imperfect structure, will regenerate.

The order Rhynchocephalia to which the tuatara belongs is now thought to be closely related to the ancestors of all the lizards, and the creature probably gives us a very good picture of what some of the primitive reptiles of over 200 million years ago were like. It has nearly as good a claim to the rather specious title of 'living fossil' as the famous cœlacanth, for it has remained virtually unchanged since the days when even the dinosaurs were young. Fossil tuataras from these distant ages have been found in several different regions, but the living form is confined to about twenty small, rugged islands off the coast of New Zealand such as Trio and Stephen Islands in the Cook Strait. Its habitat is shared by a few species of small geckos and skinks, which are the only other reptiles found in the country. In early Maori times the tuatara also lived on the mainland, but now seem to be extinct there, though the time of its disappearance is uncertain.

The islands where the tuataras live are also inhabited by large numbers of birds such as petrels and shearwaters, which riddle the ground with their burrows and manure it with their droppings. The rich topsoil supports a very large fauna of invertebrates on which the tuataras feed, while the continued movement of the birds breaks down the vegetation and provides open spaces where the tuataras can hunt.

The tuatara often makes use of the birds' burrows, although it can also dig its own. Incubating birds may be found in the same burrow with the tuatara, and it has been suggested that the birds and reptiles enjoy some special kind of amicable relationship, with the petrel living on the left side and the tuatara on the right side of the chamber. Unfortunately there is no solid scientific evidence for this pleasing idea, and tuataras have been known to feed on the eggs and young of the petrels.

Tuataras spend most of the day in their burrows, though they sometimes bask at the entrance. They are mainly active at night when they prowl about in search of food. Larger specimens are particularly partial to snails, big beetles and crickets which are chewed deliberately, sometimes for several minutes.

There have been many comments on the sluggishness of the tuatara in captivity, and on the slowness of its breathing and other vital processes. In the wild, however, even old specimens can run quite quickly for short distances, and the young are no less active than many small lizards. Adult specimens sometimes make a low croaking sound.

The tuatara lays clutches of eight to fifteen parchment-shelled eggs which are deposited in a hole about five inches deep, and then covered over with earth. The processes of development and growth certainly do seem to be much slower than is usual in reptiles. The eggs take about fifteen months to hatch, instead of the more usual two to three months incubation period of other species; the delay is probably due to the fact that the development of the embryos almost ceases during the winter. The subsequent growth rate is also very much slower than in lizards of comparable size. Dawbin believes that the tuatara does not become sexually mature until it is at least twenty years old; although the evidence for this is inconclusive, the potential life-span may perhaps be as long as a hundred years.

By comparison with most reptiles the tuatara is exceptionally tolerant of cold, and has been seen wandering about in ground temperatures as low as 45° F. Even during the winter it does not hibernate very deeply. This perhaps explains why it has been able to find sanctuary in New Zealand where the climate is cold enough to discourage competition from other large reptiles. How and when it got there, however, we do not know. At one time the animal was thought to be in danger of extinction from the attacks of domestic animals, but as the result of rigorous government protection it has now become quite common on some of the islands it inhabits. We may hope that it will survive there indefinitely, for it is certainly one of the most interesting, as well as the most ancient, reptiles known to science.

Chapter 4

SNAKES

SNAKES to many people are the most typical of all reptiles and are also largely responsible for giving the whole class of reptiles a bad name. It is true that snakes are venerated by certain primitive communities, and that some schoolboys and a few adults find them attractive pets; nevertheless, man's attitude to snakes is generally a hostile one. It must be admitted that this has some rational basis although it also owes much to ignorance and superstition. Only a comparatively small number of the many kinds of snakes are dangerous to man, and few, if any, will attack human beings without provocation. To the unprejudiced eye, many snakes are creatures of great beauty, and they all show fascinating adaptations to the various biological niches in which they work out their evolutionary destinies. Some facts about this much-maligned group of reptiles will show how mistaken it is to regard them merely with horror or suspicion.

Even the popular view that a snake is a typical reptile is quite wrong. Snakes are, in fact, among the most specialised members of their class, being really highly modified lizards which have become particularly well adapted to a limbless life. Although placed in a separate suborder, the Serpentes or Ophidia, they are still members of the Squamata, the great order of reptiles to which lizards also belong. The adaptations they have made to different habitats are almost as numerous as those found in the lizards, and the group includes some of the most expert burrowers, swimmers and climbers among the higher vertebrates. The wonderful agility of snakes, their power of swallowing large objects,

97

and the means many possess for killing their prey swiftly and surely, have also helped to bring about their evolutionary success.

To illustrate some of the fascinating qualities of snakes we will begin, as has been our practice in this book, with a few basic anatomical facts. Most members of the group have done away with their limbs more thoroughly than any of the snake-like lizards and, although a few retain rudimentary hind limbs, the majority lack any obvious traces of either pair. The backbone has, of course, become enormously elongated, and contains up to four hundred separate vertebræ, all of which, except for the first one or two behind the head and those of the tail, carry long movable ribs. The vertebræ are firmly but flexibly articulated in such a way that the backbone as a whole can bend from side to side with quite exceptional freedom. They are not capable of nearly so much up and down movement in the vertical plane, so that pictures of snakes wriggling along in vertical undulations should not be taken seriously. Between each vertebra and the next there are no less than five separate joints (Fig. 20), instead of three as in other reptiles, and higher vertebrates generally. The extra pair checks the tendency of the spine to twist around its long axis and injure the nerve cord, as might occur when a snake is climbing or constricting its prey.

The way of an eagle in the air, the way of a serpent on a rock, and the way of a man with a maid were three of the four problems which King Solomon conceded as being beyond his comprehension. None of them have been shirked by twentieth century biologists, and for illumination on the second we may turn to the work of Sir James Gray and Dr H. W. Lissmann of Cambridge, summarised in Sir James's classic work *How Animals Move* (See p. 147).

The basis of snake locomotion is the animal's ability to throw its body into a series of horizontal waves which flow continuously from head to tail. As it does this the sides of its body thrust against irregularities in the ground, such as stones and vegetation, and propel it forwards in a seemingly effortless manner. On a really smooth surface, however, such as a polished floor, a snake becomes almost helpless unless it can get into a corner or some other place where its body can

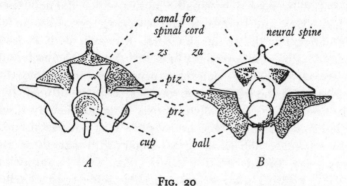

FIG. 20

Single back vertebra of grass snake (*Natrix natrix*).

A, from in front; *B*, from behind. The main joint is between the cup in the front of the body of each vertebra, and the ball on the back of its neighbour. There is also a joint on each side between the projections called prezygapophyses (*prz*) at the front of each vertebra and the postzygapophyses (*ptz*) at the back of the next, as in other land vertebrates. The additional pair of joints is between the projections known as zygosphenes (*zs*) at the front of each vertebra, and recesses, the zygantra (*za*) at the back of the next; these prevent twisting of the spine in its long axis. After R. Hoffstetter, 1939, *Archives de Muséum d'Histoire Naturelle de Lyon*, vol. 15, 31.

obtain leverage. The same principle of locomotion presumably holds good for limbless lizards, although these creatures arc far less accomplished than snakes at rapid movement over open ground, or at climbing and other acrobatics.

In most snakes the under surface of the body is covered by a single row of broad ventral scales, each of which extends across the whole width of the animal. The scales beneath the tail (the subcaudals) are usually paired. The broad ventrals are absent in legless lizards, where the belly scales are small and similar in shape to those on the rest of the body (Fig. 21, p. 104). The normal function of the broad ventrals of snakes is to catch against the ground and stop the creature from slipping backwards. In some species, however, they are used in a more active way and afford an alternative means of locomotion quite distinct from that previously described. They can be moved by small muscles which connect them with the ribs, and by raising and lowering them like the feet of a caterpillar the snake can creep forwards with its body extended almost in a straight line. But the ribs themselves do not appear to move during the process, and the old idea that a snake 'walks on its ribs' is erroneous. This 'rectilinear' type of locomotion, as it is called, is used a good deal by thick-bodied snakes such as boas and vipers. It is not practised by slender species such as the grass snake, although these also possess the broad ventral scales and their appropriate muscles. Possibly such snakes use their scale muscles when climbing, or in some other activities distinct from ordinary locomotion. In spite of their efficient method of locomotion, it must still be admitted that the speed of snakes has been much exaggerated. Even the fastest types, like the coachwhip (*Masticophis*) of North America, cannot maintain a speed of more than three or four miles per hour.

Many snakes have no special method of killing their prey. They therefore eat it alive, so that it is ultimately killed by suffocation or by the action of the digestive juices. Thus a frog just swallowed by a grass snake may hop away apparently unharmed if the snake is forced to disgorge its victim. Obviously such snakes can only tackle weak and defenceless creatures, which would be incapable of making any resistance to attack. Some, however, particularly the boas and pythons, have learnt to kill by compressing the body of the prey with their coils. Death by constriction is very quick and is probably due to stoppage of the heart and breathing. The lurid tales one sometimes reads that the victim is crushed into a pulp should be disregarded. Many other snakes have converted some of their salivary glands into organs for producing venom, and their teeth into highly effective instruments for injecting it (Figs. 23, 24, pp. 113–15). Contrary to popular belief, the tongue even of poisonous snakes is quite harmless, and though it is often used to investigate the prey before it is swallowed, it is only acting as a sense organ, in conjunction with the organ of Jacobson (p. 64).

The jaws of snakes are exceptionally mobile, being only loosely attached to the rest of the skull, and most of the bones along the jaw margins and palate are armed with sharp recurved teeth (Fig. 24, p. 123). The halves of the lower jaw are united in front only by elastic ligaments so that they can move separately in conjunction with the two sides of the upper jaw to pull the prey into the mouth—or rather, to give a more accurate description, to pull the mouth over the prey. The brain-case, on the other hand, is strong and compact, to protect the brain from possible injury which might be caused by the struggling victim. These arrangements are quite different from those found in most lizards. In the latter the upper jaw, though slightly movable, is quite firmly attached to the skull. Also the two halves of the lower jaw of lizards are generally quite firmly joined, and much of the brain is covered only by flimsy walls of cartilage and membrane.

Snakes also have several other interesting aids to swallowing. For instance, the salivary glands (Fig. 23, p. 114) are well developed and produce a copious flow which helps the prey to slip down on its one-way journey. The skin of the neck can be stretched to accommodate large objects, and the front of the windpipe, or 'glottis', can be protruded from the throat (see Plate 14) so that breathing is not obstructed when large prey is passing down the throat. Furthermore, in many snakes a part of the windpipe has taken on the function of a lung, and possibly allows breathing when the

CARL A. RUDISILL LIBRARY
LENOIR RHYNE COLLEGE

air is cut off from the true lung by the pressure of food far back in the gullet.

The reader may have noticed the use of the word 'lung' in the singular, and in fact most snakes have only the right lung at all well developed. This is very long and may extend almost down to the cloaca. The reduction or loss of the left lung is associated with the lengthening of the body and narrowing of the body-cavity so that there is hardly room to accommodate two organs side by side. With other paired structures such as the kidneys and testes, the difficulty has been overcome by spacing them at different levels. As might be expected, the same thing has happened, though to a lesser degree, in some limbless lizards.

Snakes are unable to blink, as their eyelids have been converted into a transparent spectacle. The 'third eyelid', or nictitating membrane, seems to have disappeared entirely. The outer layer of the spectacle is shed at each moult and appears like a little glistening watch-glass in the sloughed skin of the head. A snake's sight is impaired for a week or more as the time of moulting approaches owing to the accumulation of fluid between the new and old layers of the spectacle, which becomes cloudy and bluish. It clears again, however, a few days before the skin is actually shed.

Snakes have lost their ear-drums, and the stapes bone, which in most other reptiles is connected to the drum, has become connected instead to the quadrate bone of the upper jaw (Fig. 24, p. 123). This arrangement makes it most unlikely that snakes can hear air-borne sounds at all well, a view that is supported by experimental evidence. One must therefore be sceptical of tales of snakes being charmed out of their holes by music. The snake-charmer's cobra which rears up and waves its head as he plays is probably responding visually to the movements of his hands and body rather than to the sound of his instrument. Although snakes cannot hear in the usual sense, they are sensitive to ground vibrations transmitted through the bones of the jaw and skull to the inner ear. In this way they can perceive footsteps and other disturbances and slide away into the undergrowth.

It is not always easy to distinguish a snake from a limbless lizard, but some of the features we have been discussing, such as the belly scales, and the eyes and ears, often help to make the distinction. The following remarks sum up the situation. All snakes have the spectacle eye-covering and lack ear-drums, and the great majority have the characteristic row of broad belly scales. Some limbless lizards, have movable eyelids and ear-drums, though these are usually small and may be concealed by surrounding scales. None of them, however, has broad scales on the belly (Fig. 21, p. 104).

Unfortunately this useful guide lets us down in some instances. As we have seen, certain limbless lizards, such as the Australian pygopods (p. 73) have a spectacle like snakes, while in some specialised burrowers, both lizards and snakes, the eyes have become so rudimentary that their coverings are not easy to interpret without a microscope. Many limbless lizards have lost their ear-drums and their ear structure has become rather like that of snakes. A few snakes, mainly burrowers but also most of the sea-snakes, have small belly scales like lizards instead of big ones. In the really difficult cases—usually small burrowers—one may have to resort to the details of internal anatomy or the opinions of experts who sometimes disagree.

There is still much to be learnt about the social life of snakes and their mating behaviour. Some species such as the American garter snakes (*Thamnophis*) and some rattle-snakes, are more or less gregarious and may congregate in the spring mating season and before hibernation in the autumn. Hibernation in communal dens is another interesting aspect of their social life. Many snakes seem to confine their travels to a definite 'home range' such as a particular

bank or the neighbourhood of a clearing, but there is little
evidence that they defend these territories against inter-
lopers of the same species as many lizards do. The males of
some species, however, indulge in various forms of chase

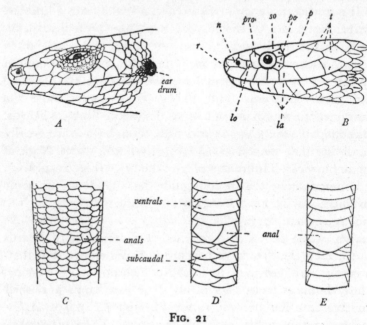

FIG. 21

Diagrams showing external differences between lizards and snakes.

A. Head of typical lizard, showing eyelids and ear-drum.
B. Head of grass snake (*Natrix natrix*), showing arrangement of head shields,
eyelids replaced by transparent spectacle, and absence of ear-drum.
After Rollinat (1934).
C. Belly scales of limbless lizard, *Ophisaurus ventralis*, an American relative of
the slow-worm. After E. D. Cope (1900, *Annual reports of U.S. National
Museum*).
D. Belly scales as seen in many snakes such as the grass and smooth snake,
with single row of large ventrals, paired anal and subcaudal scales.
E. Less usual type of belly scale pattern with undivided anal and subcaudals,
found in the rattlesnakes. In some snakes the anal may be single and
the subcaudals paired, or only some of the subcaudals may be paired.
D and *E* modified from Hobart M. Smith (1953, *Snakes as pets*, All-pets
books, Inc., Wisconsin).
Abbreviations of head shields: *la*, upper and lower labials; *lo*, loreal;
n, nasal; *p*, parietal; *po*, post-ocular; *pro*, pre-ocular; *r*, rostral; *so*, supra-
ocular; *t*, temporal.

and combat in the breeding season, and in rattlesnakes and vipers a curious ritual has been described in which two snakes rear up against each other, and each tries to push the other over. These curious displays were once thought to be courtship dances, but as the participants seem always to belong to the same sex, they are now regarded as manifestations of rivalry (Pl. 13a).

Although vision plays an important part in attracting snakes to each other from a distance, the nose and the organs of Jacobson seem to be the main sense organs involved in sex recognition at close range and in courtship. Blindfolded snakes will court frequently, but usually cannot do so if either the nose or the organs of Jacobson are put out of action. The importance of these 'chemical senses' as compared with sight in the sex life of snakes can perhaps be explained by the fact that the two sexes seldom differ very obviously in shape or colour, though the female is often the larger of the two.

In some snakes of the family Colubridæ (p. 110) the stimulation of certain touch-sensitive organs on the chin and around the cloaca is an important preliminary to the mating act. The male first rubs his chin along the female's back and throws his body into spasmodic waves which pass forwards from tail to head. He then pushes a loop of his body beneath the female to bring the two cloacæ together, and the hemipenis nearest the female is inserted. The sexual act may be maintained for over an hour, during which the female may crawl actively around, dragging the male with her.

Although we may assume that snakes are descended from lizards of some kind, the fossil record tells us practically nothing of their early history. Study of their eye structure suggests that their ancestors may have passed through a burrowing phase in their evolution during which their eyes became more or less degenerate. This would correspond with the condition found in the worm-lizards and worm-snakes today. Subsequently, it is thought, after a period of subterranean near-blindness, the snakes emerged above ground and managed, by various anatomical expedients, to restore their vision to a state of efficiency. This ingenious theory, put forward by G. L. Walls in his fascinating book *The Vertebrate Eye* (p. 632) is supported by many other aspects of serpent organisation, for example, the loss of the ear-drums, and perhaps by the great importance of touch and the 'chemical senses' in courtship. But there are also a number of specialist arguments against Walls's view, and only the discovery of new fossils is likely to clear up the mystery of the origin of snakes once and for all.

Turning next to the question of snake classification (see p. 144), we find that there are two main groups, each consisting of some four families. The first group contains all those snakes which have retained certain obvious traces of their lizard ancestry, such as rudiments of the hind limbs, a jawskeleton that is often quite firmly attached to the rest of the skull, and sometimes the presence of a fairly well-developed left lung, even though this is smaller than the right. The second group does not contain any of such comparatively 'primitive' types of snakes, but includes all the world's poisonous species.

Three of the four families in the first group are quite small. These are the two families of blind- or worm-snakes, known as the Typhlopidæ (Plate 11a) and the Leptotyphlopidæ, and the Anilidæ (or Ilysiidæ), which in the classification given (p. 144), contains the sunbeam snake (*Xenopeltis*), the pipe-snakes (*Cylindrophis*) and the shield-tails (*Uropeltis*). All three of these families consist entirely of tropical or sub-tropical snakes which burrow in the ground or live secretive lives under logs and stones. Their eyes are small, sometimes rudimentary, their necks are hardly thinner than their heads, and their tails are often exceptionally short as an adaptation to burrowing. They feed mainly on inverte-brates and such small vertebrates as lizards, and their dentition is in some cases reduced. The under surface of their bodies is generally covered with small scales instead of broad shields. Some of these creatures are very difficult to distinguish from burrowing lizards—so much so, indeed, that a learned argument is still in progress as to whether one group of worm-snakes, the Typhlopidæ, are really snakes at all or whether they should be classified with the lizards. They are of great interest to herpetologists but since they are inconspicuous, and in no way harmful to man, few other people take much notice of them.

The fourth and last family of our first 'primitive' group of snakes is known as the Boidæ. This is a very much more familiar group and contains the boas and pythons, among which are the world's biggest snakes. The family has been in existence for some 60 million years and contains almost all the most ancient snakes known, including some very large extinct forms such as *Gigantophis*, which may have been 60 feet long.

Most of the Boidæ possess quite respectable rudiments of the pelvic girdle, and hind limbs which terminate in claw-like appendages visible on either side of the cloaca (Fig. 22). These claws are generally larger in the males than in the females and, though useless for locomotion, are believed to act as aids to sexual stimulation during intercourse. The Boidæ differ from most of the other primitive snakes in having highly movable jaws and a wide gape, so that they can swallow large animals. Generally speaking, they have stout bodies and are rather sluggish, catching their prey by ambush rather than active pursuit.

The boas and pythons are usually placed in different subfamilies and have a different geographical distribution. The boas live mainly, although not exclusively, in America and the West Indies, the pythons in Africa, Asia and

Australasia. Most of them are big snakes, but some, such as the sand-boas (*Eryx*) found in arid parts of south-eastern Europe, north Africa and Asia, are quite small and have burrowing or secretive habits. Sand-boas have sombre greyish or brownish markings, blunt tails and small, though by no means degenerate, eyes. During the day they live mainly under the sand, emerging in the evening to prowl

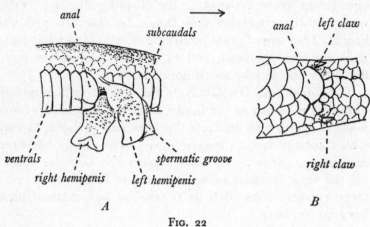

FIG. 22

A. Hemipenes of late embryo grass snake (*Na rix natrix*).
B. Cloacal region of African python (*Python sebae*), showing claws of rudimentary hind limbs. After F. Angel (1950). In both figures the arrow points towards the tail of the snake.

about on the surface in search of small rodents. One of the present authors found his first specimen of the javelin sand-boa (*Eryx jaculus*) under a sack of potatoes during the army M.O.'s routine duty of inspecting cookhouse tents pitched on an Algerian beach, and has retained a particular affection for these miniature boas ever since.

The boa constrictor (*Constrictor constrictor*; Plate 11b) from South and Central America is a more typical member of the group, growing about fifteen feet long and spending much of its time in trees. Like many of its relatives it is an exceptionally handsome snake. Its reddish-brown and

13a. Male combat dance of red diamond rattlesnakes (*Crotalus ruber ruber*).

13b. Puff adder (*Bitis arietans*) showing its fangs.

14. African cobra (*Naja melanoleuca*). The glottis can be seen in the mouth.

15a. Nile crocodile (*Crocodylus niloticus*).

15b. American crocodile (*Crocodylus acutus*) on left, and alligator (*Alligator mississippiensis*).

16a. False or Schlegel's gharial (*Tomistoma schlegeli*) of Borneo and Malaya.

16b. Marsh crocodile or mugger (*Crocodylus palustris*) of India.

SNAKES

beige markings are very conspicuous in a cage, but help to conceal it in its natural surroundings. The anaconda (*Eunectes murinus*), which is restricted to South America and Trinidad, is a much bigger snake, though not as big as many travellers' tales would suggest. It grows at least 30 feet long and there is some evidence for a record of over 37 feet. It is olive-green in colour with large dark oval markings, and is more thoroughly aquatic than its relatives. This adaptation to amphibious life is shown particularly by the eyes and nostrils being slightly shifted towards the upper surface of the head.

South America and the West Indies are the home of other species of boas such as the emerald tree-boa (*Boa canina*) (frontispiece), one of the most beautiful of all snakes, with a brilliant green background colour and white markings. It has exceedingly long front teeth which help it to capture the birds on which it preys. Curiously enough, there is a python in New Guinea with very similar colour and habits.

The three best-known pythons are the reticulated python (*Python reticulatus*) of south-eastern Asia, the Indian python (*Python molurus*) and the African python (*Python sebæ*). The reticulated python reaches an accredited length of 33 feet, though it is comparatively slender. The African python may occasionally exceed 20 feet, but this is probably the maximum length for the Indian species, which has a notably thick, heavy body. Only one other species, the amethystine python (*Liasis amethystinus*) of northern Australia, reaches a comparable size. All these snakes, when fully grown, are capable of eating such animals as pigs, goats and medium-sized deer, although they often take smaller prey. They are, of course, unable to swallow really large creatures such as horses and oxen, and seldom, if ever, attack human beings in spite of lurid stories to this effect. There are also many smaller types of python, such as the Australian carpet snakes (*Morelia argus*), and the royal python (*Python regius*), the latter a beautiful and gentle species from west Africa which spends much of its time coiled up into a ball. Some of these snakes will become very tame in captivity, and the Indian python, which combines docility with impressive size, is a favourite in show business and has even been used in strip-tease acts. Several members of the genus are also of commercial importance to man. Pythons are probably the principal source of the snakeskin used in manufacturing shoes and other articles, and their flesh is also used as human food in some parts of the world.

Unlike the boas, which produce their young alive, pythons lay eggs in clutches of twenty to a hundred or more. In some species, at least, these are brooded by the mother—a habit unusual, though not unknown, in other snakes. A brooding python will remain coiled round her eggs sometimes for weeks on end. It has been claimed that such pythons have the power of slightly raising their body temperature above that of their surroundings, as a means of incubating the eggs. The results of recent work are rather conflicting, and it would seem that only in the Indian species (*Python molurus*) is there good evidence that such a rise in temperature may occur. While these snakes are brooding, their coils can often be seen to twitch at short intervals, and it is likely that the heat generated by this muscular contraction helps to raise their temperature and incubate the eggs.

So much then for our first group of snakes. We come now to the four families of the second group which, as we have already said, lack primitive characters such as vestiges of the hind limbs, but are distinguished by containing, as well as many harmless species, all the world's poisonous snakes. The great majority of living snakes belong to one or other of these families and more than two-thirds of them are placed in the single family Colubridæ, with which we shall begin.

Many colubrids, such as the English grass snake (*Natrix*

natrix), are harmless creatures. Their saliva is only slightly, if at all, poisonous and they have no specialised fangs for injecting it. The larger kinds, however, such as the Indian rat snake (*Ptyas*), which grows 10 feet long, and the dark green and yellow whip snake (*Zamenis*) of southern Europe, although non-poisonous, can inflict painful bites. Some of these snakes are also quite effective constrictors, and the American king snakes (*Lampropeltis*) actually kill other snakes in this way. Their prey even includes the deadly rattlesnake, to whose venom they seem partly immune.

Many other colubrids have developed a rather inefficient type of venom apparatus. The back part of the big salivary gland, which lies along each side of the upper jaw just beneath the scales, has apparently been converted into a venom gland. The venom is injected into the wound through a groove in one or more of the teeth at the hinder end of the upper jawbone (Fig. 23, p. 114). This arrangement has caused these snakes to be known as 'opisthoglyphs', or back-fanged snakes, to distinguish them both from the harmless colubrids known as 'aglyphs', which have no poison-fangs at all and from the front-fanged snakes, or 'proteroglyphs', such as the cobras and sea-snakes.

In order to use their fangs effectively, the back-fanged snakes have to get a good grip on their prey and chew in the poison, which usually has a paralysing effect. In general they are not dangerous to man, although the boomslang (*Dispholidus typus*; Plate 10a) of southern Africa is a notable exception. In fact a boomslang was responsible a few years ago for the death of the famous American herpetologist Dr K. P. Schmidt. This snake is also notable for its habit of inflating its throat with air when alarmed.

Many colubrids are slender, active creatures which climb and swim well without being highly specialised for any particular habitat. The common British grass snake is a good example of this type, though some of its relatives, such as the

viperine snake (*Natrix maura*) of Europe, show some specialisations for an aquatic life. The grass snake seldom grows
much over a yard long, though individuals of five feet have
been encountered. It is often found in bracken-covered or
grassy banks near water and, like many other harmless
colubrids, feeds mainly on frogs and toads with an occasional
small fish. It is usually olive-green in colour with blackish
markings and a conspicuous yellow collar behind the head.
This collar causes it to be known in Germany as the *Ringel-
natter*, or ringed snake. It lays clutches of parchment-shelled
eggs which sometimes turn up in manure heaps. In this it
differs from certain other colubrid snakes, including some of
its close relatives, which are viviparous.

Grass snakes soon become tame in captivity and make
excellent pets for young people who are sufficiently tough-
minded not to object to their swallowing live frogs. They
hardly ever bite, but when first caught may eject a foul-
smelling secretion from a pair of large glands inside the
cloaca. This unpleasant habit, which is used as a means of
defence by certain other kinds of snake as well, decreases as
the snake settles down and becomes less nervous. Occasionally a freshly captured grass snake will feign death, lying
limply on the ground with its belly uppermost and its jaws
slightly parted and relaxed.

The colubrid family also includes the handsome Aescula-
pian snake (*Elaphe longissima*) of southern Europe, the garter
snakes (*Thamnophis*) of North America, and the smooth snake
(*Coronella austriaca*). The smooth snake occurs as a rare species
in Britain, mainly in parts of Dorset and Hampshire, where
its brownish markings often cause it to be mistaken for
the poisonous adder. Like *Elaphe* and *Thamnophis* it is,
however, quite harmless, although it resembles the adder
in bringing forth its young alive.

Some of the back-fanged colubrids have become specialised tree-snakes with extremely long, slender bodies. Among

these are the beautiful green whip snakes (*Dryophis*; Plate 9b) of India and Burma which, although often four feet long, may be little thicker than a pencil, and the African bird snakes (*Thelotornis*) which use their brightly coloured tongue tips as a lure to attract the small birds and lizards on which they prey. Another genus (*Chrysopelea*), the so-called flying snakes, can parachute downwards through the air by so altering the shape of the body that the under surface is concave.

There are several other small but interesting groups of colubrids which are usually placed in separate subfamilies. These include the aquatic snakes (*Acrochordus*) of the East Indies, which are odd, flabby-looking creatures with small granular scales of a highly complicated structure, and the egg-eating snakes (*Dasypeltis*) of Africa. The latter, which are under a yard long, feed entirely on birds' eggs, and can swallow eggs as large as a hen's. The eggs are cracked in the throat by special bony spines which arise from some of the vertebræ and project through the lining of the gullet. The shell fragments are finally regurgitated, only the egg contents entering the stomach. A full account of this interesting process is given in a paper by Carl Gans, cited on p. 146.

We must turn now from the colubrids to the members of the family Elapidæ which are all poisonous species. Some of these snakes, such as the cobras and mambas, are among the most deadly snakes in the world. The elapids possess fangs situated at the front of each upper jaw-bone (Fig. 23), and instead of being merely grooved like the fangs of the opisthoglyphs, they are usually tubular like the end of a hypodermic syringe. This type of fang has probably evolved from the simpler grooved type by the infolding of the groove until its edges meet, so that the venom can only escape from a minute hole near the tip. The fangs of sea-snakes and vipers, the other really poisonous snakes, have a very similar structure. While on the subject of fangs we should add that the fangs of snakes, like the teeth of reptiles in general, are

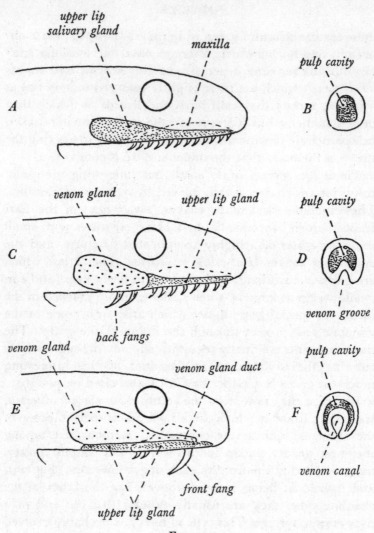

FIG. 23

Diagrams showing salivary and venom glands and teeth of snakes.
Position of maxillary bone shown in broken lines.

A. Harmless colubrid. The upper lip salivary gland produces only a more
   or less non-poisonous saliva, although the back part of it may be enlarged
   and partly distinct. B shows a cross-section of a maxillary tooth.
C. Back-fanged colubrid. The back part of the upper lip salivary gland has
   become more highly modified as a venom gland, and some of the posterior

replaced throughout the life of the animals, and each fang
has a successor behind it, ready to take its place when it
falls out. Removal of the fangs is therefore an uncertain,
and at best temporary, means of making a snake harmless.

Snake venom is not dangerous when taken by the mouth,
but when injected through the skin is rapidly absorbed into
the blood and lymph and circulated round the body, where
it does great damage to the tissues. The composition of the
venom and its effects on the victim vary a good deal among
the different kinds of snakes. Venoms are often broadly
classified into two main types, the 'nerve-poisons' and the
'blood-poisons'. The former have been regarded as characteristic of the elapid snakes such as cobras and kraits, the latter
of the vipers and their relatives. Recent work has shown,
however, that the situation is more complicated than this,
and that the venom of most snakes contains a variety of
poisons of both types, though one or the other may predominate. The venom of the Indian cobra, for example,
contains both a nerve poison which stops breathing, and a
heart poison which tends to stop the heart, these being
mainly responsible for the death of the victim. In addition,
however, Indian cobra venom contains a tissue poison
which may cause much local damage. In snakes of the viper
and rattlesnake groups blood-poisons and general cell and
tissue poisons often predominate, though the venom of
many species, especially the tropical rattlesnakes, contains
powerful nerve-poisons as well. Generally speaking, the
venom of closely related species of snakes tends to be similar
in its effects, but some exceptions even to this rule have been
noted.

---

maxillary teeth have become enlarged as poison-fangs. *D* shows such a
tooth in cross-section, with its groove for conducting the venom.

E. Front-fanged snake such as cobra. The venom gland is now separate from
the upper lip salivary gland and has a duct of its own which discharges at
the base of the specialised teeth (poison-fangs) at the front of the maxilla.
F shows the fang in cross-section; the lips of the groove have come together
to form a venom canal.

The symptoms of snake-bite naturally vary greatly, depending on the kind of snake and the properties of its venom. In many serious cases, however, there may be pain and swelling at the site of the bite, sickness, giddiness, difficulty in breathing, and finally coma, failure of the heart and breathing, and general collapse. Snake-bite in man is seldom fatal in under half an hour, though many deaths occur within twenty-four hours of the injury. Accounts of death within a few minutes after a bite are, however, reported, especially with mambas.

In all snake-bites the severity varies with such factors as the health and age of the victim, the position of the injury and the condition of the snake. If it has recently bitten something else the contents of its poison-glands may be temporarily depleted. It is impossible to say how long it takes for a snake fully to replenish its poison glands after it has used up its venom, but there is evidence that the process may be slow, even a matter of weeks.

The treatment of snake-bite is a very difficult subject on which to generalise. If the wound is inflicted on a limb, this should at once be immobilised (by tying it to some kind of splint if possible) in a dependent position to delay the spread of the venom; for the same reason the patient should move about as little as he can. The speedy application of a tourniquet above the bitten part is often recommended, but can be dangerous unless it is released at intervals. It should not be tight enough to stop the arterial pulse. The value of cutting into the wound and applying suction to it is disputed. It may be justifiable in the case of bites by really dangerous snakes, especially the big vipers and rattlesnakes, but is best not attempted if the snake is only moderately poisonous, like the English adder. Unskilled surgery with a dirty blade may well do far more harm than the bite.

The prompt injection of antiserum or antivenine is widely regarded as the most effective treatment. This is usually prepared from the blood of horses which have been immunised by receiving progressive doses of venom obtained by 'milking' captive snakes into a container. The antiserum may either be prepared against one species of snake alone—this is called 'specific' antiserum, or against two or more different species ('polyspecific' or 'polyvalent' antiserum). In places where there are several kinds of dangerous snakes and the identity of the species which gave the bite is unknown, polyvalent antisera are often used. Thus it is possible to prepare a combined polyvalent antiserum against the two types of venom, such as is made against cobra and Russell's viper venom in India.

Antisera against the bites of the more important kinds of venomous snakes are made and used in many parts of the world. Some people are highly sensitive to these preparations, however, and severe sickness and occasionally death may be caused by them. This must be borne in mind when the bites of the less dangerous kinds of poisonous snakes such as the adder (see p. 124) are being treated; it is certainly unwise to use antiserum indiscriminately in every case of snake-bite.

How many people are killed by snake-bite every year? A survey carried out a few years ago by the World Health Organisation suggested that the number might be thirty to forty thousand throughout the world, excluding Russia and China. Some authorities believe that this figure is too high, for in undeveloped countries snakes get the blame for many mysterious deaths.

Animals which habitually feed on snakes may have some resistance to the effects of venom. For example, the mongoose is partly immune to cobra venom, though it also trusts to its agility and the protection of its long fur to avoid being bitten. King snakes (*Lampropeltis*) have a partial resistance to the poison of rattlesnakes, on which they sometimes feed. It also seems that a poisonous snake is quite resistant to its own venom, and stories of snakes committing suicide by burying their fangs in their own flesh are probably more picturesque than true. Poisonous snakes are also fairly resistant to bites from other members of the same species, although the poison of other kinds of snakes may affect them.

Of all poisonous snakes cobras are probably the most familiar, and play a sinister role in many jungle tales from the outposts of the once far-flung British Empire. When annoyed they are famous for their habit of flattening their necks into a hood by raising their long neck ribs. Cobras (Plate 14) are common in both Africa and India, the Indian species (*Naja naja*) having spectacle-like markings on the back of the hood. Some species, such as the African ringhals, or 'spitting cobra' (*Hemachatus hæmachatus*), not only have very poisonous bites, but can spit twin jets of venom into the eyes of an aggressor several feet away.

The king cobra (*Hamadryas hannah*), which sometimes grows to a length of slightly more than eighteen feet, has the distinction of being the world's longest poisonous snake. Its body is quite slender, however, and its hood relatively narrow. It feeds partly on smaller snakes, and is said to be one of the few serpents that will sometimes attack a human being without deliberate provocation. However, it makes up for its aggressiveness to other species by unusual domestic virtues. The mother king cobra is the only snake known to build a nest for her eggs out of vegetation, which she piles up with coils of her body. In both this species and the Indian cobra the female, and perhaps the male also, sometimes guards the eggs, so that Kipling's account of cobra family life in *Rikki-Tikki-Tavi* may have some foundation in fact.

Cobras, with their impressive habit of rearing up and spreading their hoods, are favourites with the snake-charmer. Usually a cobra will emerge from its basket and display in front of the charmer as he sways to and fro and plays on his pipe. But as we have seen (p. 102), it is very unlikely that the instrument is audible to the reptile at all, and it probably responds only to his movements. One of the present authors once borrowed a cobra from a snake-charmer in Calcutta and persuaded it to give quite a convincing performance by waving a tobacco-pipe in front of it.

The snake-charming acts to be seen in India and Pakistan tend to be rather degraded exhibitions, for the snakes have quite often been rendered harmless by serious mutilation. Not only have the fangs been removed, but sometimes part of the upper jaw seems to have been cut away as well. Snakes treated in this way are sometimes pitted against a tame mongoose, which is of course always removed before it can kill the snake so that its master shall not be put to the trouble and expense of obtaining another. There are, however, a few reliable accounts of snake-charmers with higher professional standards who are prepared to handle cobras whose venom-apparatus has been left intact. T. H. Gillespie, in *The Way of a Serpent* (1937), describes a sect of Burmese who charm the king cobra in its unmutilated state. He shows a striking photograph of a girl—one of whose fingers had been amputated as the result of a previous bite—bending forward to kiss the head of a thirteen-foot king cobra as it sways towards her. Certainly cobras, like other poisonous snakes, can often be handled with impunity, but if one goes on doing it long enough one is very likely to be bitten. Even the most experienced snake-handlers have paid the price of over-familiarity with their lives.

The kraits (*Bungarus*), which are closely related to the cobras, are another type of poisonous snake with a bad reputation in the East. The common, or blue, krait (*Bungarus cæruleus*) which grows nearly five feet long, and the somewhat larger banded krait (*Bungarus fasciatus*) are the best-known species. These snakes are mainly nocturnal and, like the king cobra, feed to a large extent on other snakes. The blue krait sometimes frequents the neighbourhood of houses and is therefore potentially dangerous; it is, however, extremely unaggressive although it is the cause of some few casualties. The venom of the banded krait is probably rather less powerful than that of its relative, but little is known of its effects on man.

Related to the kraits are the small, beautifully banded coral snakes found in parts of America, Africa and Asia. Some of the American forms, such as *Micrurus*, are of particular interest in that certain harmless snakes which inhabit the same regions resemble them closely in colour. This may be an example of mimicry of the same kind as is shown by certain harmless flies which mimic wasps.

The mambas (*Dendroaspis*), perhaps the most dreaded of all African snakes, are also members of the elapid group. The commonest forms are the black mamba (*Dendroaspis polylepis*) and the green mamba (*Dendroaspis angusticeps*). These are now usually regarded as separate species, rather than as different races of a single species of snake. The black mamba, which is one of the world's largest poisonous snakes, sometimes reaches a length of fourteen feet. It varies with age from dull green to black and, like all mambas, is extremely agile both on the ground and in the trees. It has the disturbing habit of raising the front part of its body high off the ground so that it can deliver a bite on the hands or face. Although some field workers believe that the ferocity of this snake has been much exaggerated, the cautious traveller is likely to live longer if he regards it as an extremely dangerous animal. Its venom is certainly very potent indeed, and stories of a single individual killing two or three people in rapid succession are hardly likely to spur the prudent to intimacy. The more brightly coloured green mamba is rather smaller and apparently less dangerous. It also spends more of its time in the trees than the black mamba.

Apart from the animals already mentioned, the family

Elapidæ also includes all the poisonous snakes of Australia. Here likewise some very formidable reptiles are to be found. The taipan (*Oxyuranus scutellatus*) is the biggest, and a full-grown specimen will reach a length of at least ten feet. Perhaps fortunately this snake is confined to the north-eastern part of the continent and even there is comparatively rare. The tiger snake (*Notechis scutatus*), which has brown and yellow markings, the brown snake (*Demansia textilis*), the black snake (*Pseudechis porphyriacus*) and the mulga snake (*Pseudechis australis*; Plate 10b) are also large and dangerous reptiles, the neurotoxic venom of the tiger snake being particularly deadly. Like most elapids, these snakes are usually swift and slender. An exception is the death adder (*Acanthophis antarcticus*), which is stout and sluggish, and in many ways resembles the vipers.

The third family of our second group of snakes is known as the Hydrophiidæ, and includes the exceptionally interesting kinds of snakes which live in the sea. Although they fall far short of the legendary sea-serpent in size, the biggest have been known to reach a length of over eight feet. Sea-snakes are probably descendants of the elapid family which have taken to marine life, developing deep, vertically compressed tails for swimming, and valvular nostrils which can keep water out of the nose. Some experiments carried out on the *Galathea* Deep Sea Expedition a few years ago showed that certain species, at least, could survive forced submergence for over two hours before they drowned.

Most sea-snakes never come ashore voluntarily and move only with difficulty on land. Owing to the shape of their tails and hinder part of their bodies they tend to flop over on their sides when out of the water, and most of them have lost the broad ventral scales which help other snakes to move on land (see p. 99). Their young are born alive in the water, except in a few species which have retained the power of terrestrial locomotion and come ashore to lay eggs.

Many of these snakes are beautifully coloured, with transverse bands or rings, while the back as a whole is darker in hue than the belly. Such colours probably help to camouflage the snake, the bands breaking up its outline as it crawls among corals, and the shading of the upper and lower surfaces making it hard to see in the water, where the light comes from above. One genus of sea-snakes, *Microcephalophis*, is remarkable for its shape, the head and front part of the body being extremely slender in comparison with the rest. It has been suggested that this creature may prey on eels living in deep crevices of coral.

Sea-snakes are found in the warmer parts of the Indian and Pacific Oceans, but as a rule, they stay in coastal waters. There is one genus, however, known as *Pelamis*, which ventures freely into the open sea. This snake has crossed both the Indian Ocean and the Pacific, and has established itself on the coasts of east Africa and the west of southern America. It is by far the most widely distributed member of the group.

Although sea-snakes feed mainly on fishes, their neurotoxic venom is extremely lethal to mammals. In fact the venom of one species, *Enhydrina schistosa*, is perhaps the most powerful of any snake studied, at least under laboratory conditions. They are not aggressive creatures, but bathers and fishermen are bitten from time to time, and a sea-snake research centre has recently been set up at Penang in Malaya to investigate their habits and the properties of their venom.

The members of the last family of snakes, known as the Viperidæ, which includes the vipers and rattlesnakes, possess the most efficient and highly specialised venom apparatus of all snakes. The construction of their upper jaw bones differs considerably from that of the elapids and sea-snakes. Whereas the latter have their fangs more or less fixed in the erect position, the vipers and rattlesnakes have the great advantage of being able to fold them back against the roof of the mouth

SNAKES

when they are not in use. Consequently the fangs can become extremely long—over an inch in a big puff adder or rattle-snake—and can inject the venom deep into the body cavity

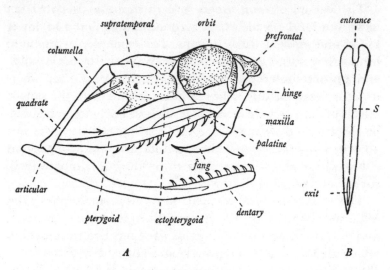

FIG. 24

A. Skull of horned viper or asp (*Cerastes aegyptiacus*) seen from the side. Modified from M. Phisalix (1922, *Animaux venimeux et venins*, Masson, Paris). The erection of the fang is brought about by the pterygoid being pulled forward by muscles and imparting its movement to the ectopterygoid and ultimately to the maxilla, which rotates at a hinge on the prefrontal bone. Arrows show direction of movement. It is often stated that the pterygoid is pushed forward by the lower end of the quadrate, but this is doubted by some modern workers. The columella is also known as the stapes (p. 102).

B. Fang of viperine snake seen from in front, showing entrance and exit of venom canal and suture (*s*) between lips of venom groove, converting it into a canal. The suture is often absent and is less marked than that shown by the fangs of many front-fanged snakes. After M. Smith (1954).

of a small animal. The mechanics of this arrangement depend essentially on the fact that the short fang-bearing bone of the upper jaw is able to pivot freely on the facial skeleton, as is shown in Fig. 24.

After delivering its bite a viper or rattlesnake usually withdraws in a flash instead of hanging on as a back-fanged and some front-fanged snakes will do. The victim is seldom

123

approached again until it is dead. If it has moved some distance away before succumbing, the snake trails it at leisure, using its tongue and organs of Jacobson.

The venom of most vipers and rattlesnakes is noted for its serious local effects, which are mainly due to the action of blood and general tissue poisons. For example, it produces hæmorrhages and great swelling near the site of the wound, and a bitten limb sometimes turns gangrenous. Death, when it occurs, may be due either to heart failure or to the slower effects of extensive tissue damage. It is unlikely to be painless or elegant, and we may hope that Cleopatra's 'asp' was not a horned viper, as is sometimes maintained, but an Egyptian cobra whose bite is more likely to produce a comparatively speedy and painless death.

The Viperidæ are divided into two subfamilies, the Viperinæ, containing the vipers of Europe, Africa and Asia, and the Crotalinæ, containing the pit-vipers and rattlesnakes, which are found in America and Asia. The adder (*Vipera berus*; Plate 12a), the only poisonous snake inhabiting Great Britain, is in many ways typical of the smaller viperines. Unlike some of its cousins, however, it is extremely tolerant of cold, living at altitudes of over 9,000 feet in the Alps and ranging as far north as the Arctic Circle in Scandinavia and Finland. It occurs in almost every county in the British Isles, except in Ireland, where the common lizard is the only reptile found. Adders like ferny banks and can often be seen basking on the edges of large clumps of bracken. They are also quite common in certain types of marshy country and will take to water on occasion although, unlike grass snakes, they do not remain in it for long periods.

The adder is a shorter but relatively stouter snake than the grass snake, and seldom grows longer than a couple of feet. The scales on the top of its head are also smaller and differently arranged (Fig. 25). Incidentally, the size and arrangement of the scales is a character which distinguishes

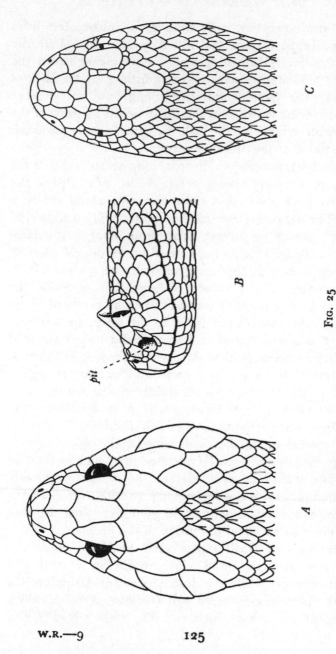

FIG. 25

Heads of *A*, grass snake (*Natrix natrix*), after M. Smith, 1954; *B*, side-winder rattlesnake (*Crotalus cerastes*), showing sensory pit, after L. M. Klauber, 1956; *C*, adder (*Vipera berus*), after M. Phisalix, *Animaux venimeux et venins*, 1922.

most of the vipers not only from grass snakes, but from many colubrids, elapids and allied species. In colour the adder is normally brownish with a dark zigzag down the back and a V-shaped mark, often indistinct, at the back of the head. The females and the young tend to be more reddish than the males, and the snake called by some of the older British naturalists 'the little red viper' is only a reddish juvenile phase of the ordinary species.

Adders feed mainly on lizards, slow-worms and small rodents, particularly young voles. As in most vipers, the young are born alive, and there are often about ten in a brood. The tale that the mother adder will swallow her new-born young to protect them from danger is almost certainly a fable. It is perhaps based on an optical illusion, the young merely disappearing suddenly beneath the belly of the mother. The presence of large fœtuses inside the body of a pregnant adder smashed open by repeated blows may also have encouraged belief in the story. In this connection it is interesting to find that similar beliefs are held in the U.S.A. about rattlesnakes, which are also viviparous.

The bite of the adder is seldom fatal to man, though it is likely to be more serious in children than adults. Conservative forms of treatment, such as immobilising the bitten limb, resting the patient in bed and looking after his general condition, together with some psychological reassurance are usually the best. Heroic measures, such as incision of the bite should be avoided. For the reasons previously mentioned (p. 117) it is wisest not to give antiserum except in very severe cases or, sometimes, in young children. Morton (1960) gives an excellent discussion of the problem.

Other types of small vipers such as *Vipera aspis*, and *Vipera ammodytes*, the sand viper, occur in central and southern Europe, while the deserts of north Africa are the home of the sandy-coloured asp (*Cerastes cornutus*), which has a small horn above each eye. The night adder (*Causus rhombeatus*), and the mole vipers (*Atractaspis*)—which differ from most other vipers in being burrowers—are found in central and southern Africa.

Among the largest vipers are the puff adder (*Bitis arietans*; Plate 13b), widely distributed in Africa; the Gaboon viper (*Bitis gabonica*; Plate 12b), which has a more restricted range; and the oriental Russell's viper (*Vipera russelli*), which is the 'Daboia' or 'tic polonga' of many planters' tales. These snakes really fulfil the popular conception of a viper. Though none of them grow much more than four feet long, they have stout bodies and large V-shaped heads. The puff adder has dull brownish markings, but the other two have rich colours suggestive of a Persian carpet which add somehow to their sinister appearance. The Gaboon viper is further distinguished by having a pair of short horns at the end of its nose. These snakes are normally sluggish, but if trodden on strike fiercely and inflict terrible bites with their long fangs. The venom of the Russell's viper is renowned for its blood-clotting properties: it has actually been put to medicinal use in the treatment of hæmophilia and certain other blood diseases where the patients' blood fails to clot in the normal way so that intractible bleeding may result from a small wound.

Rattlesnakes and other pit-vipers of the subfamily Crotalinæ differ from the vipers just described in having an extremely interesting sense organ known as the sensory pit on each side of the head between the eye and the nostril (Fig. 25). This is a complicated structure containing a thin membrane stretched between its walls, and is very richly supplied with nerves. Experiments have shown that it responds to heat radiation and is sensitive to minute differences of air temperature—for instance, a variation of less than 0·2° C. These organs probably help the snake to find warm-blooded prey in the dark.

The name pit-viper is given to both the rattlesnakes and

to those crotaline snakes which do not possess a rattle. Nevertheless some of the latter species, such as the crossed viper (*Trimeresurus alternatus*) of southern Brazil, are able to make a rustling sound by vibrating the tail tip very rapidly against vegetation. Central and South America and the West Indies are the real home of the group, and here we find such formidable snakes as the fer-de-lance (*Bothrops atrox*), and the eleven-foot bushmaster, the largest of the pit-vipers, whose scientific name, *Lachesis muta*, means 'silent fate'. In North America the group is represented by the water moccasin or cottonmouth (*Agkistrodon piscivorus*), a big, black, ugly snake which lives in swampy parts of the deep south, and the copperhead (*Agkistrodon contortrix*), a smaller terrestrial species. Some pit-vipers, such as the Indian bamboo viper (*Trimeresurus gramineus*), are tree-snakes, while others, such as the Himalayan viper (*Agkistrodon himalayanus*), are mountain-dwellers which have been recorded at heights of up to 16,000 feet. This, incidentally, is the greatest height at which any living snake is known to live.

Rattlesnakes (Plate 13a) are particularly associated with the U.S.A., but some forms are found further north in Canada, and others in parts of Latin America. They are also common in Central America; a rattlesnake in the claws of an eagle sometimes figures on the Mexican coat of arms.

The unique feature of a rattlesnake is, of course, its curious rattle. This is made up of a number of interlocking horny pieces which, when vibrated some sixty times a second, produce a sinister high-pitched buzz. The rattle is sounded to warn off intruders who might be dangerous, and often allows the snake to save its venom for another occasion. It plays no part in rattlesnake social life, and it is very doubtful if a rattler can even hear the sound itself. The very young snake possesses only a single 'button' at the end of its tail and adds a segment at each moult, often several times a year. Eventually a 'string' of some six to eight segments is formed, the 'button' remaining at the end. At this length the rattle usually breaks so that very long strings of twelve segments or more are uncommon.

The biggest rattlesnakes are the diamondbacks (*Crotalus adamanteus* and *Crotalus atrox*) and the tropical rattler, or cascabel, of South America (*Crotalus durissus*). The scientific names of these animals are particularly evocative, the first two meaning respectively, 'iron-hard rattling one', and 'savage rattling one'. These deadly reptiles are all massive, heavy snakes which grow to about seven or eight feet long. The timber rattlesnake (*Crotalus horridus*) is the common species of New England and the north-eastern U.S.A. This is probably the species which figures in Oliver Wendell Holmes's novel *Elsie Venner*—a book recommended to all imaginative herpetologists. Among the many smaller types is the desert rattlesnake or 'sidewinder' (*Crotalus cerastes*), which closely parallels the asps of north Africa and Asia. Like these it has a horn over each eye (Fig. 25), and moves in a characteristic sideways fashion which is more efficient over soft sand than the normal type of serpentine locomotion. Rattlesnakes have even left their mark on the history of the Wild West, for every old-time cow outfit, it is alleged, employed at least one dubious character known as Rattlesnake Joe or Sidewinder Charlie.

Chapter 5

CROCODILES AND THEIR ALLIES

W<small>E</small> come now to what in many ways is the most exciting and majestic of the four orders of living reptiles, the crocodilians. These magnificent animals, more than any others of their class, call to mind a picture of the great era, known as the Mesozoic, when reptiles dominated the earth. Although different from the great dinosaurs of that time in many physical details, they are yet the only surviving representatives of the subclass Archosauria ('the ruling reptiles'), to which the dinosaurs also belong. In bodily structure, and probably also in habits, crocodilians have altered very little since this distant era, which came to an end some seventy million years ago. Moreover, the various crocodilian types living today, though usually placed in three different groups, differ very much less from each other than do the different kinds of lizards and snakes, and even the different kinds of chelonians.

Of the true crocodiles, one of the largest and most dangerous species is the estuarine crocodile (*Crocodylus porosus*) which ranges from the Bay of Bengal eastward across Malaya to the Solomons, New Guinea and north Australia. It inhabits the mouths of large rivers and coastal swamps, and sometimes swims out to sea, a habit which probably accounts for its wide distribution. A skull presented to the British Museum (Natural History) over 100 years ago is alleged to have belonged to a 33-foot individual, but this estimate of length is probably exaggerated. Nowadays 20 feet is perhaps near the maximum length of the species. The largest living species are dwarfed by the giant 50-foot crocodile *Phobosuchus*, which lived in Cretaceous times and probably preyed on young dinosaurs.

The Nile crocodile (*Crocodylus niloticus*; Plate 15a) is the best known of the African types, and extends throughout the greater part of the continent, from Egypt (where it is now almost extinct) to the northern parts of Natal. It may, exceptionally, reach a length of 20 feet, and like the estuarine crocodile, has a bad reputation as a man-eater. Instances of it attacking small boats with outboard motors have recently been reported.

This crocodile, perhaps the leviathan of the book of Job, was well known to the writers of the ancient world. Herodotus, the famous Greek traveller and historian of the fifth century B.C., has much to say about it and was probably the first to describe the association between crocodiles and such birds as the spur-winged plover (*Hoplopterus spinosus*) and the common sandpiper (*Actitis hypoleucos*). The latter has actually been seen to pick food, possibly leeches, from the crocodile's open mouth—a habit reported by Herodotus but not confirmed until quite recently by reliable observation. In later times the Roman emperors are reputed to have introduced crocodiles into the arena, although we have no details of the type of spectacle in which they participated.

Thanks to the researches of Dr Hugh Cott of Cambridge, we know more about the habits of the Nile crocodile than of any other crocodilian except, perhaps, the American alligator. Cott's survey of stomach contents of a large sample of these crocodiles killed in various parts of Uganda shows that the young animals feed mainly on insects and other invertebrates, but as they get older fish come to form the main element of their diet. Later still they turn to eating other reptiles, birds and mammals, and in the largest group (crocodiles over thirteen feet long) these replace fish as the principal food. Quantities of pebbles are also swallowed by the bigger individuals, and Cott believes that these act as ballast, enabling the animal to remain steady in the water and even to rest on the bottom. This crocodile, incidentally, is in great need of protection from hunters who are interested only in the short-term profits to be made from the hides, which are used in the manufacture of handbags and other readily saleable articles. The depredations of greedy and irresponsible men of this kind have led to the virtual extinction of the animals in many parts of Africa.

Several other kinds of crocodiles are found in different parts of the world. The marsh crocodile or mugger (*Crocodylus palustris*; Plate 16b), which has a relatively shorter and broader snout than the estuarine and Nile crocodiles, occurs in India and Ceylon. It is confined to inland waters, and is a somewhat smaller animal than its African cousin, seldom exceeding a length of between ten and twelve feet. Although dangerous to many kinds of herbivorous animals which come to the waterside to drink, it seldom attacks men. The American continent, the home of the caimans and alligators, shortly to be discussed, also possesses several species of crocodile, and one of these, *Crocodylus acutus*, occurs as far north as the southern parts of Florida. This is among the largest of all crocodiles, with a maximum recorded length of over 20 feet, and it is also distinguished by having a rather narrow snout.

Two narrow-jawed fish-eating crocodiles, *Crocodylus cataphractus* and *Crocodylus johnstoni*, both of moderate size, are found in west Africa and northern Australia respectively. Africa is also the habitat of two small and very short-snouted species placed in a separate genus, *Osteolæmus*. *Osteolæmus tetraspis*, the commoner form, is an odd-looking pug-nosed creature with large liquid brown eyes, quite unlike the greenish-yellow eyes of most other crocodilians. It grows about six feet long, but the related *Osteolæmus osborni* from the

Congo seldom exceeds a yard, and is the smallest living crocodilian.

The gharial (*Gavialis gangeticus*) from northern India can easily be distinguished from almost all other living crocodilians by the extreme length and slenderness of its snout. This is set off abruptly from the head almost like the handle of a frying pan, and in mature males a curious swelling develops near the nostrils at the tip of the upper jaw. The animal grows very big, up to 20 feet long, but even when adult feeds mainly on fish, which it catches by very rapid sideways snaps of its long jaws. A creature of similar external appearance, which is nevertheless only doubtfully related to the gharial is the so-called 'false gharial' (*Tomistoma schlegeli*; Plate, 16a) of Borneo.

The best-known of all crocodilians is the American alligator (*Alligator mississippiensis*; Plate 15b), which lives in the swamplands of the southern U.S.A., and is common in the Florida Everglades. Adult alligators are almost black, but the young have light yellow markings on the flanks, and traces of these may persist into later life. The snout is broad and rounded at the tip, being in this way distinguished from the more pointed snout of most crocodiles. Another distinction is based on the fourth tooth in the lower jaw, which fits into a pit in the upper one and so cannot be seen when the mouth is closed. In crocodiles, on the other hand, this tooth is lodged only in an open notch and is therefore always visible; indeed, the teeth generally are more conspicuous than in the alligator. But these and other differences between alligators and crocodiles are really quite trivial, and no one but herpetologists would worry about them but for the fact that the creatures happen to have been given different names. The word 'crocodile' comes from the Latin *crocodilus*, and was given to the animals when the Romans colonised north Africa, whereas 'alligator' is a corruption of the Spanish *el lagarto*, meaning 'the lizard', which originated when the first

Spanish settlers occupied the southern parts of North America.

Alligators have now been hunted out of some of their favourite haunts, though fortunately some states have recently given them a certain amount of legal protection. Like other crocodilians they grow fast under favourable conditions when young, and increase in size from about eight inches to over a yard in their first two years of life. At six years old, when they are ready to reproduce, they have reached a length of about six feet. After this, growth slows down very noticeably and the males ultimately become much bigger than the females, growing up to 12 feet or more. A captive specimen is known to have lived for 56 years, the longest recorded life-span of any crocodilian. Wild alligators usually hibernate in the winter in dens dug out of the muddy bank.

Studies of the alligator's food suggest that invertebrates such as insects and crustaceans form a large proportion of the prey. The larger individuals also eat frogs, fish, snakes, turtles, water birds and mammals—in fact almost anything which they can catch. They seldom attack man, however, and in captivity are usually the most docile, as well as the hardiest, of crocodilians.

Another smaller species of alligator (*Alligator sinensis*) is found in China, where it inhabits the grassy swamps of the lower Yangtze valley. Little is known of its habits but, like the American species, it is reputed to hibernate in burrows.

The caimans, or jacares, are the characteristic crocodilians of South and Central America, and figure prominently in books by travellers in these regions, such as Charles Waterton's famous *Wanderings in South America* (1825). Their main distinguishing feature is that they have bony scutes beneath their belly scales as well as those on the back. The black caiman (*Melanosuchus niger*) is the largest species, sometimes exceeding twelve feet in length, while the dwarf caiman (*Paleosuchus palpebrosus*), with a maximum length of four feet, is one of the smallest members of the order. Small specimens of the broad-nosed *Caiman latirostris* from Paraguay and Brazil are often imported into this country and are sometimes sold as 'baby alligators'. They do well in captivity, but require a higher temperature than alligators in order to remain active and healthy.

The crocodilian body is beautifully adapted to an amphibious, predatory mode of life. For instance, the eyes and nostrils are placed on the upper surface of the head so that the crocodile can see and breathe when the rest of the body is submerged. Also the nostrils are opened and closed by special muscles, sealing off the inside of the nose when the animal dives. The nasal cavities are drawn out into long tubes surrounded by bone which open far back into the throat just in front of the orifice of the wind-pipe or trachea. This region can be shut off from the rest of the mouth by valves so that the crocodile can open its jaws under water (as it does when it is drowning large prey) without inhaling water itself (Fig. 26). Furthermore, it is able to breathe during the process if it can manage to thrust its nostrils above the surface, for the air passes straight back through the nose into the windpipe behind the valves without having to go through the mouth.

The ears of crocodilians are protected by scaly flaps which can be raised and lowered, exposing the ear drums. Normally, however, the flaps are kept shut, except for a small slit-like aperture at the front, which opens when the animal's head is out of water and apparently suffices for hearing; this sense seems more important in crocodiles than in most reptiles, but the animals are presumably deaf when submerged, as their ear-flaps are then tightly closed (Fig. 26).

The muscles which close a crocodile's jaws are extremely strong, and big specimens are sometimes able to drag cattle and horses into the water. But the muscles which open the jaws are comparatively weak, and it is said that a man can hold a crocodile's mouth shut with his hand. Anyone wishing to try this experiment should bear in mind the creature's ability to make surprisingly quick side-snaps. One sometimes reads the statement, attributed originally to Herodotus, that it is the upper jaw of a crocodile, and not the lower, which is hinged to the skull. This is incorrect, but if one watches a

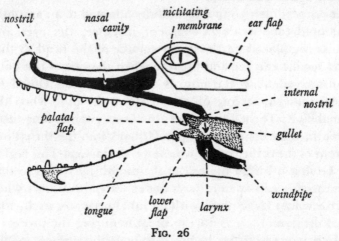

Fig. 26

Diagram showing air passages of a crocodilian in longitudinal section. The palatal flap and the lower flap behind the tongue can be brought together to form a valve, so that water cannot enter the larynx, windpipe or gullet from the mouth when the crocodile opens its jaws under water. At the same time the animal is able to breathe if its nostrils are above the surface. The airway is shown in black; the arrow shows the direction of flow of the air breathed in.

crocodile open its mouth with its chin on the ground one can see the source of the error. The head as a whole has to be tilted back on the neck in order to make the movement, so that the upper jaw appears to be the one that is mobile. But actually, as it carries the skull with it, the effect is an optical illusion. Incidentally, the habit of gaping the jaws when lying on the bank seems to be a method of temperature control, since the evaporation of fluid from the lining of the mouth would have a cooling effect.

136

The crocodile's sharp conical teeth are suitable for holding prey rather than for cutting it up, and animals too large to be crushed and eaten whole are usually torn to pieces. To achieve this the crocodile usually seizes hold of a limb and twists it violently this way and that until something gives way. Well-fed crocodiles are said to hide their prey in holes until it is partly rotten, though whether this is really true is doubted by modern authorities.

Like most other reptiles, crocodiles are able to replace their teeth over and over again, and it has been estimated that the nilotic species has had 45 generations of teeth when it has reached 13 feet. Whether very old animals ever lose their teeth in the wild is unknown; even the biggest skulls in museums seem to have a complete dentition. In captivity, however, crocodiles may lose the ability to replace their teeth, possibly as the result of some disease or dietary deficiency, and the very old alligator 'George' who lived for over 40 years in the London Zoo had only a few short teeth when he died.

Although crocodiles spend long periods basking or lying motionless in the water, they can sometimes move very quickly. For instance, if startled when lying on the bank of a river they slide with amazing speed into the water and enter it with hardly a splash. On land they often walk with the body held high off the ground, and one can then readily see that the hind legs are considerably longer than the front ones. This has been regarded as evidence that the ancestors of crocodiles walked on their hind legs, like birds and many dinosaurs. Recent work suggests, however, that the crocodiles were always quadrupedal.

The tail is the main swimming instrument, and also serves as a very effective defensive weapon. When the crocodile is swimming fast the legs are pressed against its sides, but the partly webbed feet are sometimes used for slow paddling. There are five claws on the front feet, and four on the hind.

During the breeding season male crocodilians become quarrelsome. Some species, such as the American alligator, are very noisy, and are constantly roaring and bellowing at each other, especially during the night. Mating takes place in the water and is seldom witnessed, but Cott describes a kind of pre-nuptial display in which the female Nile crocodile rears up out of the water with her open jaws pointing to the sky.

The female always either covers her eggs with sand or constructs some sort of nest for them out of plant debris. The eggs themselves are oval and hard-shelled with a maximum length of three and a half inches. The clutch may vary from thirty to ninety. In some crocodilians quite advanced parental behaviour, by reptilian standards, has been described. In the Nile crocodile, for example, the mother remains on or near her eggs throughout the thirteen-week incubation period in a torpid state without feeding. At the time of hatching the young croak, and this acts as the signal for their mother to release them from the nest, which is buried beneath a foot or so of sun-hardened sand. The mother is also said to defend her newly-hatched young against intruders, and even to escort them down to the water like a duck.

Both eggs and young are as liable to attack by a variety of predators as those of turtles. Large monitor lizards are particularly partial to crocodile eggs and will dig them up at once if the female leaves them unguarded. Once the young crocodile has reached a certain size, however, it becomes almost immune from attack except by man and larger individuals of its own species. Although crocodiles are mainly hunted for their hide they are also used as food in some parts of the world and a steak taken from the base of the tail is said to be good eating.

With these few brief facts about the crocodilians we must bring our account of the world of reptiles to a close. In the space at our disposal it has not been possible to indicate more than a very small part of the interest that these remarkable animals can offer to the curious naturalist, but we are confident that the works listed in the Bibliography will fill in most of the missing details for those who care to consult them. We conclude with the hope that the study of reptiles may afford to at least some of our readers as much pleasure and interest as it has given to us.

APPENDIX A

MANY who read this volume will be familiar with the use of scientific names. For those who are not, however, a few remarks on the function and principles of zoological nomenclature may be helpful. Ever since the days of antiquity naturalists have tried to devise some way of cataloguing the immense variety of living things which they were trying to describe.

The modern system of naming and classifying plants and animals is based on the work of the great Swedish naturalist Carl von Linné, usually referred to as Linnæus, who lived during the eighteenth century. It is organised as follows. First the whole living world is divided into two great groups, known respectively as the animal and vegetable kingdoms. Organisms within these groups are then ascribed to a number of major subdivisions, known as 'phyla' (from the Greek *phulon*, meaning a 'race' or 'stock'), according to differences in their basic anatomical structure. Each phylum is then subdivided into smaller groups called 'subphyla' and 'classes', and then into 'orders', 'families', 'genera', and 'species'. Additional categories, such as suborders, super-families, subspecies, and so on, are also sometimes introduced to define still further the position of a particular group of organisms.

All these divisions of the natural world are known by names derived from the Latin and Greek languages which, although apparently somewhat remote from everyday life, really simplify very greatly the discussion of any organism in its scientific context. For instance, suppose we wish to talk about the ordinary domestic dog in scientific terms. We will find first that it belongs to the major division, or phylum, of the animal kingdom known as the Chordata, or animals with notochords. (The notochord is a rod-like structure running down the back which precedes the growth of the vertebral column in the embryonic development of all vertebrates. It also belongs to the very large group of chordates which make up the subphylum Vertebrata, or the animals with backbones. Narrowing the field, we next find that the dog belongs to the sub-division of vertebrates known as the class Mammalia, or mammals. These can be defined as warm-blooded, usually hairy animals which suckle their young by means of milk glands. In order to define the dog's status among the mammals, we must assign it to a sub-division of this class, the 'order' Carnivora, which consists characteristically of flesh-eating mammals, and then to the 'family' Canidæ, or dog-like carnivores within that group. Beyond this again we arrive at the 'genus' of the animal, called *Canis*, which at last expresses what we may best call its 'dogginess'. Even so we have not quite got our domestic dog scientifically catalogued. The genus *Canis* contains several different types of 'doggy' creatures and in order to make it really clear that we are talking about the domestic dog and no other, we have to add the extra name *familiaris* to its generic name, writing it scientifically thus: *Canis familiaris*. This double-barrelled name is then what we call the 'specific' name of the animal, defining its status in the animal kingdom without any shadow of doubt; the word *familiaris* on its own represents what is known as the 'trivial' name. We can, of course, go on to talk about different 'varieties', or 'races' of *Canis familiaris* (e.g. poodles, fox terriers, spaniels, boxers, etc.) but all these still belong to the same species. A further category known as the subspecies is often used to designate the 'varieties' of certain species which occur in the wild, though it is not used for the different varieties of domestic dog. Similar principles of classification apply not only to the mammalian dog, but also, of course, to birds, reptiles, amphibians, invertebrates, plants, and indeed to every other kind of living thing.

The scientific name of an animal or plant written on a zoo

or museum label is therefore really an extremely simple and accurate way of defining the exact identity of the organism. It corresponds closely to the Christian name and surname of a member of our own species, *Homo sapiens*, as listed, with the surname first, in a telephone directory or other alphabetical register.

APPENDIX B

A SHORT CLASSIFICATION OF THE LIVING REPTILES OF THE WORLD

ZOOLOGICAL classification and nomenclature, like other man-made systems, are liable to error and variation. The reader who consults other works on reptiles will find that the systems used often differ in certain particulars from that given here, which is based on Professor A. S. Romer's *Osteology of the Reptiles*. This is particularly true with regard to classification into families and other smaller units, which is, to some extent, a matter of personal opinion. One possible reason for discrepancy is the fact that workers may disagree about the zoological relationships of a particular group so that each may give it a different systematic position. More often, however, the disagreement will only concern the status which the group should be given; one worker may regard it as a family, whereas another may feel that it only deserves the status of a subfamily. Many workers distinguish a considerably larger number of families of living reptiles than are listed here; the various types of primitive snakes, for example, are usually divided into six, instead of four families, the sunbeam snake (*Xenopeltis*) and the shield-tails (*Uropeltis*, etc.) being placed in separate families from the pipe-snakes (*Cylindrophis*, etc.). Romer, however, has drawn these distinctions on the subfamilial level, and although some authorities disagree we feel that there are certain advantages in following his practice.

APPENDIX B

For reasons of space the following classification is carried only to family level. A few small families not specifically discussed in the present book are listed for completeness but no English names are attached to them. The order in which the various groups are set below does not always conform strictly to the order in which they are mentioned in the text.

CLASS REPTILIA

Subclass Anapsida
  Order Chelonia or Testudinata (tortoises, terrapins, turtles)
    Suborder Pleurodira
        Family Pelomedusidæ (side and snake-necked terra-
            pins)
          „   Chelyidæ (matamata, etc.)
    Suborder Cryptodira
        Family Dermatemydidæ
          „   Chelydridæ (snappers, mud and musk ter-
             rapins)
          „   Testudinidæ (land tortoises, pond and box
             terrapins, etc.)
          „   Cheloniidæ (sea turtles)
          „   Dermochelyidæ (leathery turtle)
          „   Carettochelyidæ
          „   Trionychidæ (soft-shells)
Subclass Lepidosauria
  Order Rhynchocephalia
        Family Sphenodontidæ (tuatara)
  Order Squamata
    Suborder Lacertilia, or Sauria (lizards)
        Family Iguanidæ (iguanas, basilisks, anoles, horned
            toads, etc.)
          „   Agamidæ (frilled and bearded lizards,
             agamas, etc.)
          „   Chameleontidæ (chamæleons)
          „   Gekkonidæ (geckos)
          „   Pygopodidæ (scale-foot lizards)

Family Xantusiidæ (night lizards)
    ,,   Teiidæ (tegus, ameivas, etc.)
    ,,   Scincidæ (skinks)
    ,,   Lacertidæ (common, sand and green lizards etc.)
    ,,   Cordylidæ, or Zonuridæ (girdle-tailed and plated lizards)
    ,,   Dibamidæ (including only a worm-like burrower of doubtful systematic position)
    ,,   Anguidæ (alligator lizards, slow-worm, etc.)
    ,,   Anniellidæ (containing a single footless burrowing genus)
    ,,   Xenosauridæ
    ,,   Helodermatidæ (gila monster, escorpión)
    ,,   Varanidæ (monitors)
    ,,   Lanthanotidæ (earless monitor)
    ,,   Amphisbænidæ (worm lizards)
Suborder Ophidia, or Serpentes (snakes)
Family Typhlopidæ (worm snakes)
    ,,   Leptotyphlopidæ (worm snakes)
    ,,   Anilidæ, or Ilysiidæ (pipe-snakes, sunbeam snake, shield tails, etc.)
    ,,   Boidæ (boas, pythons)
    ,,   Colubridæ (includes both harmless (e.g. grass snake) and fanged (e.g. boomslang) types)
    ,,   Elapidæ (cobras, kraits, mambas, taipan, etc.)
    ,,   Hydrophiidæ (sea-snakes)
    ,,   Viperidæ (vipers, pit-vipers, rattlesnakes)
Subclass Archosauria
Order Crocodilia
Suborder Eusuchia
Family Crocodylidæ (crocodiles, gharial, alligators, caimans)

BIBLIOGRAPHY

Note: Books and articles marked with an asterisk contain long bibliographies. Those marked (†) are important studies of the natural history of a single species or group.

ANGEL, F. (1943). *La vie des caméléons et autres lézards.* Gallimard, Paris.

* ANGEL, F. (1950). *Vie et mœurs des serpents.* Payot, Paris.
   The two valuable books by this author cover many aspects of structure, function and life-history.

* BELLAIRS, ANGUS D'A. (1957). *Reptiles.* A volume in the Hutchinson University Library, Hutchinson, London.
   An introduction to reptile structure and function.

BELLAIRS, ANGUS D'A. (1959). Reproduction in lizards and snakes. *New Biology,* no. 30, pp. 73–90.
   An introduction to the subject.

† BLAIR, W. FRANK (1960). *The rusty lizard: a population study.* University of Texas Press, Austin.
   An account of the life-history of a small lizard (*Sceloporus olivaceus*).

BOGERT, CHARLES M. (1959). How reptiles regulate their body temperature. *Scientific American,* vol. 200, pp. 105–120.

* † BOGERT, CHARLES M. and DEL CAMPO, RAFAEL MARTÍN (1956). The gila monster and its allies: the relationships, habits, and behaviour of the lizards of the family Helodermatidæ. *Bulletin of the American Museum of Natural History,* vol. 109, pp. 1–238.

BOULENGER, G. A. (1913). *The snakes of Europe.* Methuen, London.
   An excellent semi-popular account with a good introduction on snakes in general.

* CARR, ARCHIE (1952). *Handbook of turtles: the turtles of the United States, Canada, and Baja California.* Comstock Publishing Associates, a division of Cornell University Press, Ithaca, New York; Constable, London.
   Deals primarily with the American species but contains a good introduction to chelonian organisation.

BIBLIOGRAPHY

CARR, ARCHIE and THE EDITORS OF LIFE (1963). *The Reptiles* Time, Inc., New York.

* † COTT, HUGH B. (1961). Scientific results of an enquiry into the ecology and economic status of the Nile Crocodile (*Crocodilus niloticus*) in Uganda and Northern Rhodesia. *Transactions of the Zoological Society of London*, vol. 29, pp. 211–356.

* DAREWSKI, I. S. and KULIKOWA, W. N. (1961). Natürliche Parthogenese in der polymorphen Gruppe der kaukasischen Felseidechse (*Lacerta saxicola* Eversmann). *Zoologische Jahrbucher* (Systematics section), vol. 89, pp. 119–176.

† DAWBIN, W. H. (1962). The Tuatara in its natural habitat. *Endeavour*, vol. 21, no. 81, pp. 16–24.

EIBL-EIBESFELDT, I. (1960). *Galapagos*. Translated from the German by A. H. Brodrick. Macgibbon and Kee, London.

* † FITCH, HENRY S. (1960). Autecology of the Copperhead. *University of Kansas Publications, Museum of Natural History*, vol. 13, no. 4, pp. 85–288.
A thorough study of a snake's life-history.

FITZSIMONS, VIVIAN, F. M. (1962). *Snakes of Southern Africa*. Macdonald, London.

GADOW, HANS (1901). *Amphibia and reptiles*. A volume in the Cambridge Natural History. Macmillan, London.
Still invaluable, though superseded in some ways.

* † GANS, CARL (1952).The functional morphology of the egg-eating adaptations in the snake genus *Dasypeltis*. *Zoologica*. New York, Vol. 37. pp. 209—244.

* † GANS, CARL (1960). Studies on amphisbænids (Amphisbænia, Reptilia). I. A taxonomic revision of the Trogonophinæ, and a functional interpretation of the amphisbænid adaptive pattern. *Bulletin of the American Museum of Natural History*, vol. 119, pp. 129–204.
A fascinating, but technical study of adaptation to burrowing life.

* GOIN, C. J. and GOIN, O. B (1962). *Introduction to herpetology*. W. H. Freeman, San Francisco and London.
A useful introduction to the scientific study of amphibians and reptiles.

BIBLIOGRAPHY

GRAY, JAMES (1953). *How animals move.* Cambridge University Press, London. Also issued by Penguin Books, Harmondsworth, 1959.
Contains an account of snake locomotion.

* † HARRIS, V. A. (1964). *The Life of the Rainbow Lizard.* Hutchinson, London. Describes social life of *Agama* in Africa.

HELLMICH, WALTER (1962). *Reptiles and amphibians of Europe.* English editor, A. Leutscher. Blandford Press, London.
A well-illustrated account of the European species.

* † KLAUBER, LAURENCE M. (1956). *Rattlesnakes.* 2 vols. Published for the Zoological Society of San Diego by the University of California Press, Berkeley and Los Angeles.
A magnificent compilation of facts and theories about rattlesnakes.

MERTENS, ROBERT (1960). *The world of amphibians and reptiles.* Translated from the German by H. W. Parker. Harrap, London.
An up-to-date account with splendid illustrations.

* MORRIS, RAMONA and MORRIS, DESMOND (1965). *Men and Snakes.* Hutchinson, London. Deals with mythology, snake-charming, etc.

MORTON, T. C. (1960). Adder-bites in Cornwall. *British Medical Journal,* no. 5195, July 30th, pp. 373–376.

NOËL-HUME, IVOR and NOËL-HUME, AUDREY (1954). *Tortoises, terrapins and turtles.* Frederick Muller, London.
Contains useful directions on keeping those animals.

OLIVER, JAMES A. (1955). *The natural history of North American amphibians and reptiles.* Van Nostrand, New York, etc.
An excellent semi-popular account; life histories are exceptionally well covered.

PARKER, H. W. (1963). *Snakes.* Robert Hale, London.
An excellent semi-popular account of the organisation and life of snakes.

* PARSONS, JAMES J. (1962). *The green turtle and man.* University of Florida Press, Gainesville.
An account of green turtle fisheries throughout the world.

* POPE, CLIFFORD H. (1956). *The reptile world.* Routledge and Kegan Paul, London.
A fine general account with many good photographs.

BIBLIOGRAPHY

* POPE, CLIFFORD H. (1962). *The giant snakes.* Routledge and Kegan Paul, London.
    A good popular account of the big boas and pythons.

ROLLINAT, RAYMOND (1934). *La vie des reptiles de la France centrale.* Librairie Delagrave, Paris.
    Full of information on the habits of the local species, many of which are also found in Britain.

* ROMER, ALFRED SHERWOOD (1956). *Osteology of the reptiles.* University of Chicago Press, Chicago.
    The definitive technical work on the skeleton of reptiles, living and extinct.

ROMER, ALFRED SHERWOOD (1959). *The vertebrate story.* University of Chicago Press, Chicago.
    Contains the best semi-popular account of reptile evolution.

ROSE, WALTER (1950). *The reptiles and amphibians of southern Africa.* Maskew Miller, Capetown.
    A useful popular account.

SCHMIDT, KARL P. and INGER, ROBERT F. (1957). *Living reptiles of the world.* Hamish Hamilton, London.
    Fairly short, but very informative; beautiful plates.

* SMITH, MALCOLM (1954). *The British amphibians and reptiles.* A volume in the New Naturalist series. Collins, London.
    An admirable work on the British species.

* WALLS, GORDON LYNN (1942). *The vertebrate eye and its adaptive radiation.* Cranbrook Institute of Science, Michigan.
    A technical work which nevertheless contains much fascinating information on the reptile eye.

WORRELL, ERIC (1963). *Reptiles of Australia.* Angus and Robertson, Sydney, London, etc.
    A synoptic account of the Australian species.

Those who wish to follow up the literature on reptiles further will find the classified bibliography known as the *Zoological Record*, issued annually by the Zoological Society of London, an invaluable source of references. The journals *Copeia* and *Herpetologica* (published in the U.S.A.) and the *British Journal of Herpetology* contain many articles on reptile natural history. They are available in libraries such as those of the Zoological Society of London and the British Museum (Natural History).

INDEX

INDEX